CW00968700

The NIGHT WAGES

MARTIN SHAW

CISTA MYSTICA PRESS
Devon, England

Illustrations © 2019 by Martin Shaw.
Cover art by Martin Shaw.
Cover and typesetting by Michael Martin.

Printed in Devon, England.

British Library Cataloguing-in-Publication Data
A catalogue record for this book is available from the British Library
ISBN 978-1-9160035-0-7 (paperback)

I went to the desert in winter,
I found a hut and I wrote this book.

Everything happened, just like this.

the
silent
waves

the
silent
waves

WHAT HAPPENED

Table of Contents

The Underneath VII

PART ONE: OH MOON ENCHANTED SEA

Chapter One   Firebird Language 3
Chapter Two   Man on Raft, Talking to Himself 21
Chapter Three   Shameless 27
Chapter Four   Island of the Locked-in Secret 31
Chapter Five   My Heart was Broken the Moment I Set Eyes on You 45

PART TWO: CORMORANT UNFOLDS

Chapter Six   The Queen of All Wild Horses 59
Chapter Seven   Woman is a Wild Thing 75
Chapter Eight   The Sherwood Croft 87
Chapter Nine   There is a Man Who Never Dries Out 93
Chapter Ten   Bone Memory 111

PART THREE: RIDDLES OF THE NET-MENDER

Chapter Eleven   Spirit Bear and the Bleak Shore 119
Chapter Twelve   The Mood of the World in Sleep 133
Chapter Thirteen   Becoming Crocodile 143
Chapter Fourteen   What Mayaki Heard at the Smokehole 159

PART FOUR: THE HOUSE OF BEASTS AND VINES

Chapter Fifteen   The Door of Mercy is Still Open 169
Chapter Sixteen   Cista Mystica 177
Chapter Seventeen Into the Marvellous 187

Coda 209

"Sweet love, renew thy force."
Shakespeare, *The Sonnets* (LVI)

"Walt. There's no dignity in love. Come home."
Ruth-Ann Miller, aged 77, sending a message to Walt the Trapper,
TV series, *Northern Exposure*

The Underneath

"I've been lost many times upon the sea."
Federico Garcia Lorca

The little boy is sitting on a sandy towel on Torquay sea front. 1979. He's quite still, but everything else is moving.

Crackles of sand have violated his ham sandwiches. He wonders if that's why they have their name. He's proud of this thought, but keeps it to himself. He enjoys the sharp kick of mustard that makes him realise he's munching on his dad's by mistake. He gazes out at lithe bodies and everywhere is the scent of suntan lotion. He feels far away from it all. A way away.

He grew up near the sea, so it was salt water first. Before rivers, or lakes, ponds or streams. The taste that lives in teardrops. It was the big, dangerous stuff. He knows the older lads sometimes swim to a black rock in the distance, and girls with floating voices from other countries watch them do it.

He's thinking about those young men, splish-splashing their fledgling valour over the waves. There's a bunch of them just a few metres away.

These lovers, don't they know about the Underneath?

These county darlings, who will one day work the breweries, launderettes, building sites and hotels of Torquay, these county darlings, who, for one summer day in 1979, are utterly magnificent. Should be garlanded in flowers as their shuddering bodies arise from freezing waves and flop nonchalantly down in front of the admiring, temporary eyes of these foreign bodies. These true sons of Poseidon. Soon the girls will be gone—a couple of letters at best—and then the wintering sets in, and the hotels will be empty.

This is the last great decade of the bay, before the heroin moves in.

Boy blinks with concern. *But do the big boys know about the Underneath?*

Underneath is fulsome mermaids who send up sultry red ropes of longing, a longing that grabs, shudders, shakes, makes lunatic the barnacled, bobbing Brixham tugs, and pulls all the delirious fisherman down.

Underneath is a confluence of roaring Celtic Sea Gods, gambling hard, losing it all every night, weeping and drinking and crooning love stories to the women up on the rocks: that's the Sirens, enflaming the nerve endings of the waves with enough glamour to cause even mighty Orion to halt his star-spun peregrinations and consider a dive. Millions of years old and they catch him out every single night.

This nautical underswill is what causes every furious scrap on the cobbles, what causes those beauteous and nutty old ones in Paignton nursing home to wave their sticks and yell of that one night with dear Dotty so many years ago: alive, alive in the ever greenness of things.

Like a mad concertina, the fanged blue teeth of the world stretch and compress and slap asunder all our neat little plans and ambitions. Makes us crazy in a way the gods find charming, occasionally beautiful.

Even safe up on a hill, at night the boy hears the slap! slap! slap! of the waves licking at his front door as the world attempts to tip him under. Seaweed crawls through the letterbox, foam lurches the roof and he quietly opens his window to the spray. He gazes out and sings:

Oh Moon Enchanted Sea

Do the boys that swim to the dark rock know that every ninth wave is a little higher than the rest, and called The Ram? *Do they?*

Underneath is whale skulls with candles lit in the eye sockets, blue-dark bottles of rum nested in lonesome black weeds, and the thrubbing heart of all things pulsing and twisting in the heretic currents of this, the pagan west. Splash! Splash! Splash! That's where the action is, Jack. *But do the boys know?*

And how does the kid know?

Never to be much of a swimmer, much has changed for him with goggles. It was keeping his head above the waves that he wasn't any good at.

Life before goggles meant murky grey shapes zipping through an indistinct haze as he bobbed optimistically about, growing steadily weaker by the second. Life after goggles was a whole other game. Where once was chilly blur now presides a visible, regal, underneath. The strength of his whole body changes in relationship to what he can now see.

He is now able to submit to the compulsion to go down.
He can finally sink.
He can finally be a ruin.

A nautical savvy arrives without one extra length of the school pool. Throw in a snorkel and he can now groove about for as long as he wants. It is that abrupt, the change.

He will see magnificent things down there.

Oh Moon Enchanted Sea

PART ONE

Chapter One

Firebird Language

"As long, long ago, I launch my boats of bark."
Czeslaw Milosz

The boy who fretted of the Underneath is all grown up now. Years have passed, decades, and all the ordinary catastrophes that come with them. But of late, they have come faster and deeper. Of late he has lost all his mirth. Four-square wisdoms turned out to be built on sand after all. So, an end to all that.

It's time to go home. To the real. Arcadia, Camelot, the back of the Wardrobe.

He has crafted a raft with his daughter. In some tangible fashion they have been building it her whole life. Since first she opened her almond-shaped eyes on a spring evening twelve years before, and he fell under the hooves of all that is true and mysterious in this world.

Soon they will carry swinging lanterns and leave their cottage, their tottering piles of old books, their seemingly endless roast chickens, wood fires and dozing cats, and meander down to the river at the bottom of the garden. After a time they will slosh their craft out onto a fast moving river and go a-voyaging.

Don't know when they will be back. Haven't even rung the school. For a moment they stand around and admire their craft, heads cocked, smoking imaginary cigars. They have callouses from patting each other on the back.

They are going to sail out on the wilder shores of love. The man remembers that phrase from a book. *The Wilder Shores of Love.* God almighty.

The man of the Underneath is trying to get them south. The return to Greece. To Aphrodite herself. See what she has to say to men who got their heart really, properly broke. To give libation, to peer into the blue smoke at her ancient temple, to fill the whole world with wild flowers. His tears have all the salt of Mongolia in them.

Is this really wise? Some friends would counsel taking a warship, or a cruise liner, or at very least, a well-armoured tug boat. But a raft? Practically twigs.

But if they have true questions about love, then what can possibly protect them from its furies? Not steel, or stature, or tugging engine. It's hardly a risk-free endeavour. They are not weighed down with horoscopes, internet dating, or even travel insurance.

Strap me to the mast my brothers, I want to hear The Song of the Sirens, The Song of the Spheres, The Music of What Is. I am sick of the world's beeswax blocking these ears, I am sick to my stomach of sucking on the lotus fruit. I will not deny the Garden of the Lovers a moment longer.

Love.

Not the stuff some therapists approve of: the reduced, off-the-boil, not in-love-but-loving kind, but finding a place for the indecent, howling hunger strike of a feeling that scythes all in its path. The perilous. The Chapel Perilous. Dionysus riding the leopard.

But not 'place' like something settled. No agriculture please. They want chunks of meat, blood on chin, flickering fire, the wild rumpus. Not a village. Not a town. No school run. There's absolutely no planning permission where they're heading. It's a night sea journey and their compass is ecstatically drunk, indiscreetly lonesome and prone to abrupt changes of location.

Love.

Not as a neurotic garnish for sexual desire, or a temporary, politic hallucination for wealthy couplings, but as a sustainable, dangerous, uninsurable, risk-aggravated fit of telling the truth. With stages, and delicate negotiations and repentances, with tango twists and sudden, excruciating slips. With long periods of silence. Love as something utterly and profoundly important. As a thing worth taking seriously.

They imagine that sometimes the raft will run on land, with mud underfoot, crashing through long periods of foliaged darkness and flicking thorns before breaking the hell out into sudden views of waterfalls and hummingbirds. We all cheer at such a moment.

Then it's back skimming, skimming like a stolen coin over blue Russian ice, and charging down into the Lascaux caves with Bonnie and Clyde as our guides, holding nothing but a spluttering candle of tiger fat. They point at the shadows on the breathing walls and they coo under an antelope robe.

For some of this foolishness they may end up trudging on foot, or secreted within the wingspan of a condor, or on the sturdy back of a Carpathian steed, yip yip yipping over the whipping grasses and unconsecrated, vampiric Mountains.

The point is they don't know yet. The fidelity is to the journey, not the mode of transport.

The captain of the raft is not heroic, but the things he stands for certainly are.

His heart, he has noticed of late, has started to become only partially visible. A dyslexia of feeling, a strange jumble, then lots of quiet, or numbness. Sometimes he gestures to his chest and notices it's simply not there, but buried far away under a tree. What alarms him is that many seem to have no problem with this arrangement.

This is why they are setting sail. For the both of them. To find the heart that folks at large may wish you to forget. To un-colonise their imagination.

The man thinks this:

The shrinks have got it wrong, the marital mediators and the priests have got it wrong, your friend with an expression like she's sucking on a rotten lemon describing her tortured years with Julian has got it wrong. The ones that make love small, conditional, and robbed of holy stature have got it wrong. He's left the coffee morning and will never see them again.

They will learn to dance on the tips of spears. Their sentences are boats burnt on the beach of love's great islands. There is no pretence at retracing our steps. They are committed.

It's going to be chaotic at times. Art is the enemy of the well made. Robert Motherwell said that. A lover's home is designed to collapse magnificently. Loving repair has its erotic fulfilment. On every fridge of every great poet is taped, *'the only sense of security we have is a false sense of security'*.

As they push out and catch the current, the girl asks questions: *What is love? Why do things hurt? Why do people go away?* And when she talks of love, she's not asking for Agape, she's wanting to discuss the big guns—the unforgettable, Amor. So he will croak what he can.

Nightingales sweep to the left and the right of the raft as they push out into the dark.

Ah, but you can't outrun your daughter's questions. No dad can.

✳✳✳

Little one. There is an old Russian notion that very early every morning, the Firebird sweeps low through the forest, with her majestic, solitary head bent as if she is listening for something precious. I think her procession through the woods is the arrival of dawn itself. Some believe—okay, I believe—she remembers a time when humans used to offer loving, inventive and passionate words to her. She flies low to catch just a moment of such gorgeousness in her fine and praiseworthy feathers. As the years go by, her heart aches at the absence of such love-speech. Lifetime after lifetime, nobody comes. Or if they do, the speech is false somehow, and we sense it—hopefully we sense it. There are plenty of glittering traps under the snow of the false singers.

Well, I think some of us are a little like her. I do. Even after all the therapy, and divorces, and psychologising, the bracing cold showers of rationality, somewhere we remember the old coo-call, and we sweep through the lonely glades for even an echo of the sound. We want to be beheld in the old way, even—or especially—in a climate of absolute amnesia to such a deep yearning.

So dad asks daughter if she's ever felt glimpsed like that. Why would such a thing matter? Then they talk about Firebird feelings, and flap their wings.

She also seems to know that she's talking about something dangerous and alive. And that there's a kind of contract with loneliness that is signed if you agree to take the shape that such things call forth in you. At least sometimes.

But not to fly the dusky woods at all? Well, she'd have to have another kind of father for that conversation. And, for a little while longer at least, she still wants to know what he thinks about things.

So he continues:

Some grown ups have become suspicious of romantic love. Yes, it's very powerful. It has consequence.

But the gods forgive lovers. And so should we. Handled well, and given the tempering of time, it is an enormous gift to the world beyond this one. All the horses of your little heart will bend their head to fresh water when it arrives. Nothing else is quite the same. And there is more at stake than just the desire of the lovers. It can be a libation. That desire goes somewhere holy. The gods absolutely adore it, like catnip, like an exquisite tequila, like you and I adore Aslan, like wood smoke on a crisp October day, like the melodious chant of bells at a summering Dartmoor wedding. It gives them delight. It's an altar. So it's for more than us for a start. That really changes the perspective. It can be devotional.

Do you remember Dad's friend Robert? The white-haired old man? He wrote a poem for his wife, Ruth, and some of the lines are here:

I know how much ruin love can bring
But at night I hang around the orchard
Hoping to catch one breath from the lovers' tree.

He wrote that as an old man, not a teenager. He knew exactly what he was writing. I suspect he and his wife paid a heavy mortgage on their love several times over in the early days. But that debt became a beautiful, sweet-smelling, handmade robe that they cuddled under when sitting up late gazing at the stars. It forged them in some way. They have treasure beyond all measuring.

Love derails world-weary strategy, loosens cynicism from your bones, laces every single one of your gorgeous cow-like lashes with a complete re-boot of wonder. You guide your cattle through the Altai mountains in just one night and arrive at a green, slow-swishing Mediterranean sea with hot, moon-white sand between your toes. It is the greatest thing. Stay away from anyone that tells you otherwise. I mean turn around and walk away.

Love gives us our stories.

It re-opens us to a world in full disclosure, calls down angels and raggedy children and happy dogs and hot nights and blue moons. And yes, trouble too. It is an enormous invitation.

The "problem" is not the experience, it's that we live in a time that has often forgotten the dance steps to approach such an invitation. It is an attempt to make us bigger, not smaller. A life already cooked in beauty and art, and helping other people and animals and glittering spirits of goodness tempers us to its magnificence, rather than attempts to neuter it.

People use this ghastly word "projection". Scratch that. The word Jung used before he came up with that was much better: *rapport*.

It's not what we smother them in from our own fevered imaginings, but what radiates through them from the Otherworld. What stands behind them. We behold, bear witness, not fantasise.

So prepare well. Cultivate your inner life whilst reaching out to the world. Wander your oak valleys, linger in ornate chapels at dusk, get thrown out of the tavern at midnight, be kind, kiss the wounded, fight injustice and protect, protect, protect all the trembling bells of delight that you notice out of the corner of your eye when everyone else is oblivious. Value yourself, know yourself, don't be naive, but don't be afraid of love. Carry it.

The air is full of birds of all shapes and sizes, hurtling about. Over the years, you will see and admire many flashing feathers and big characters that swoop overhead and sometimes block out the sun. Others have a lovely poetic chirp, and do little pirouettes to attract your attention. Some will twirl around pretending they have a broken wing. Some really do. It's good to see all this life occurring all around. We can spend many years just grooving around in all this activity and liveliness.

But one day, maybe when you are much older—and this is the deepest of the things we're talking about—something else may happen. You will notice a bird that flies at your altitude. They may not have the same patterning on the wing, but they fly at the same height. They fly alongside. They really, truly do. This is the moment. This is the moment. This is the moment.

This is the moment that the Firebird bends her noble head for.

Dear one, you should know that this is as rare as one of her feathers. Almost a rumour. Something a handsome priest may murmur to you. But no. It does exist. I know—I've beheld it. This is called Amor. And the moment you experience it, you realise that the loneliness of your years without it is the debt paid for its arrival.

If you don't know something about loneliness I'm not quite sure you can really know Amor.

Prepare. Preparing well means that you can absorb the intensities rather than be completely flattened by them. That's not to say rationality has a great deal of say. But, if the courtship is true (and be prepared for many false starts in this regard, I'm afraid—it's called an educated heart), then you can rise to meet it, like the prow of some northern ship on the nine waves, not cowed and half crazed with want. Become mighty and settled in yourself. Or at least pretend and work up slowly. This usually takes a long time, but the seeds are tickling away under the soil from very early on, jiggling about. As your father I will sing over the seeds with you, shoulder to shoulder. Know the animal you are and you will be a little less likely to be seduced by the detritus of the world.

Some enlightened souls will tell you that you can have the experience of Amor entirely on your own, in complete containment. I don't think so. Risk is part of it; visibility is part of it; contact is part of it. You can't find your soul-kin without it.

No one is complete. No one can absolutely provide everything you ever longed for. But that's not really the point. It shouldn't make them small, but rather, interesting. But it is the compass of your heart that will give you the discernment between the swooping birds that showboat the sky and that steady one that shows up on the same sweet current of air.

⁂

The girl is thoughtful, throws a sea biscuit at her dad's head, and feels the weight of the waters underneath their fragile boat. She wraps herself in a blanket and continues her questions: *How did we get here? And what is the nature of those that dream of water?* She always had a poetic turn of phrase. These are wisdoms that require a deeper source. What she really wants is stories. So the storyteller begins.

Sedna's Comb

There was a woman who dreamt of drowning.

Once upon a time, in a village in the far north. A place of blue snow and vast thoughts.

A man grew angry at his daughter's refusal to marry. But no suitor from the village flew at her altitude, could witness her many immensities. He grew ashamed of her. He took her out in his kayak and chucked her overboard. As she tried to claw her way back on board, he cut her fingers off, and she sank under black water. From each finger sprung fish, whales, seals.

Down in coal-black depths, she learnt to live in a different kind of way. A kind of house built around her, she became a goddess of the sea-beings: all those that know the dark, the cold, and can survive at great pressure. When any travesty to the world above occurred she would grow furious and the hunting would not be good. The village would starve. A rough cloud of anger would appear around Sedna, she would be obscured from view, but her wrath everywhere. When the world is on fire, to lose contact with Sedna is a terrible thing. So the village would send the shaman down to see her.

The Shaman has a seal-hole in their heart where magics rise and fall.
The Shaman ghost-dances through history.
The Shaman refuses not the perfume of Gethsemane.
The Shaman moves through culture's own conscience to get to the very bottom.

It is an arduous journey, descending ladders of blades that cut your feet till blood clouds the waters. Know this: it is not a journey that anyone would ever want to make. But suddenly, there they are, attending the blurry clouds of Sedna's anger. And it is there that the One-Who-Is-A-Light makes covenant with Sedna; courts her with drum-thump and the grandeur of their ordinary tears. Such courting causes a hole to appear in her wall of anger and the shaman climbs through.

Their sweetness becomes a comb, and there in the dark the shaman combs all the tangles out of Sedna's hair, and gently braids it. Her anger simmers then settles, and those desire paths open up again from the deep freeze, move their divine tendrils up and out over the land. Many hours later the shaman will be pulled half-dead from the black water, arms filled with wild flowers.

❋❋❋

The Huntress

There was a woman who dreamt of the sea.

Back when there was a village called Tikeraq, and there lived a man and a woman. But it's not really their story I'm telling. It's their daughter's story I'm telling.

She was a huntress, famed for both her stamina and her strength. She was different from the others. The other hunters simply couldn't keep up with her. Sometimes she'd play a little game and let the men go out hunting on their kayak. Only when they had disappeared would she set out, and soon she'd be way beyond them. That was just how it was.

Her father would accompany her: he was happy to steer while she rowed with her powerful arms, throwing the harpoon too. One day they were at the end of a trip and were heading back to shore. Of a sudden a beast of the deep came upon them, snarling and gnashing. As the beast came right to the rim of the kayak the huntress hurled her harpoon at it. That very same moment her eyes rolled back in her head and she fell into a faint.

When she awoke she found herself kneeling upright on a thin stretch of beach between sea and land. Betwixt and between she was. Like she was praying.

Not knowing where on earth she was, she took a westerly direction and followed the curves of the coastline. For a long time there was no sign of humans until she came across little chips of wood on her path. She knew she'd soon encounter somebody.

Kept walking. Pad pad pad.

Soon she came across a kayak. As she was admiring it she heard a voice from everywhere and nowhere say:

"My kayak has trapped someone. If it is a man I will slaughter him, if it is a woman she will live."

The very second, the moment, she heard these words a man came running to her over the snow. A man of power. A shaman. He took her by the arm into his igloo and made her his wife.

Part of his magic was that he could make his kayak travel over both land and water, and most of the time he was out in the vast grey or the vast white whizzing about, working his charms.

The huntress did not hunt very often now. She stayed home, and attended to the tasks of the igloo.

Every day she was left alone, a small boy came to visit. One minute he was not there, the next he was. She never once saw him arrive. But such boys are always hungry and she would always feed him before he disappeared again.

One day the boy-that-comes-from-nowhere lifted one pale finger and spoke, "Grandmother needs to speak to you." Such is it with generosity.

They walked over snowy hill
They walked over snowy hill
They walked over snowy hill

And into the igloo of the old woman. Straight away the old one spoke, "You have fed one who is hungry. You have fed one who is dear to me. My very grandson. Because of this I have gratitude to you and want to help you. The man who you have married is a dark power and he grows sick of you. Soon he will be killing you. He has had many wives before, and when he grows weary of them he kills them. His ice house is full of them. When you make love with him, if you glance down to the floor beneath you, their faces will float up under the ice."

The huntress felt the truth of it. He had been hostile and distant to her for a long time now. The old woman continued, "The other wives would not feed the boy so I would not help them, but you I will. There is only one magic I possess that will save you."

At this the old one fell into trance, and described a scene as if she was carving it out of the very air:

"Here you see your husband coming to end you.
Take this seal-skin pail I give you. It has something deep in the bottom of it.

He is at the igloo. He looks for you. He thinks you have escaped and is very angry. How dare you escape. He is in his magic kayak. He is coming he is coming he is coming. He knows you are here. Take this pail in your hand!

When the bow of the kayak appears throw the pail on top of it. He is coming he is coming he is coming."

That very moment the bow of the handsome kayak burst into the old woman's igloo. The huntress threw her rounded pail over the sharp jut of the kayak and she fell into unconsciousness.

When she awoke she found herself kneeling on a thin stretch of beach between sea and land. Betwixt and between she was.

Like she was praying.

Like she was praying hard.

She started walking west, following the curve of the coast. Sometimes she saw things: she saw a huge animal, a huge wild animal the like of which she'd never seen before, lying by an igloo. She walked on to people who gave her food and let her curl up and fall asleep in the shelter of their igloo. The men asked her, "Will you stay with us?"

She replied, "I am always heading west. I keep walking."

"In the west there are beings that will kill people. They slaughtered our child. Take this little knife, it is the only weapon that will keep you alive."

A man produced a little knife from his belt. The handle was so short it was hard to handle, but its size made it easy to conceal, and it was very deadly.

To curate its magic required spit. The blade was moistened with saliva and the man lodged it, handle first, into the igloo wall. Despite herself, the huntress was compelled to press her body swiftly onto the razor sharp copper blade. It was all she could think of. Having given his demonstration, the man gave it to her.

Easy to conceal. Hard to handle. Very deadly. Animated by spittle.

Now, all you storytellers, what does that remind you of?

She walked deeper into what the west is, and many ogres fell irresistibly onto her blade. Ghoul after ghoul.

Longer she walked she walked she walked towards the place that these terrors come from. Longer she walked and walked and walked and she realised the name of the place.

Tikeraq.

The place that breeds darkness is the place she came from.

When she entered her home village a terrible one set upon her. She was set upon by the chief of the ogres.

It was her father. The one who steered her kayak.

She wetted her tongue with spittle, and told him a story that cuts like a knife.

Of hunting with her father, of harpooning a monster, of marrying a sorcerer, of feeding a hungry boy, of a curved magic that defeats a straight magic, of always walking, of the gifting of a weapon that defeats even the death-energy of the west.

As she spoke, to ensure her power, she placed her blade in the wall of her father's igloo. He would have hurled himself upon it had she not pulled it free at the climax of her story.

The father was scared, but the spell was broken. Knife or story, he couldn't tell. Couldn't recognize the difference. Is there a difference? He spoke:

"When you disappeared, all I had left of you was the darkness you harpooned. I took the bad beast to shore and we ate it. Since then this hunger to eat humans has blazed through our settlement. No longer."

In the early morning, before the people wake, father and daughter quietly push their kayak over the waves.

✳✳✳

The Woman Who Became a Fox

There was a woman who dreamt of a lake.

Not of the ocean, not of the river, but of the lake that she grew up by, with her people. It would show her true reflection.

She did not live there anymore, she lived with her husband on the edge of a vast forest.

Did I tell you he was a terribly ugly man? But if you asked his wife she would say she didn't mind his ugliness.

Did I tell you he had only one eye? But if you asked his wife she would say she didn't mind his one eye.

Did I tell you he was secretive? Now that—that—his wife could not stand. It ate away at her.

Every day he would track forest paths hunting and return at dusk, with no word of what had happened on his day. Nothing. He would chuck the game onto the table and slouch by the fire till he went to bed.

She resolved to follow him, to see how the day revealed itself to him.

Next morning she trailed after him into the forest. To her surprise as he walked he did something she'd never heard him do before. He started to whistle a lively tune. In fact he even picked up his pace and danced a few steps. What was happening?

He came to a glade and stopped. Peering up through the branches at the rising dawn he stopped whistling and started to sing. A powerful, beautiful song. She crouched down and witnessed the unfolding. Because as he sang his shape began to change, to leap, to twist.

He became an even UGLIER, one eyed, secretive man!

If he was bad before, he was now a catastrophe.

Powerful moment in the wife's life. She made a decision.

She would no longer share a hut with such a man. The marriage was over. Her life with him was over. Free as a bird.

With excitement she turned and ran further into the forest than she'd ever been before.

She was happy as she ran.

A huge hand grabbed her off the path. A hand belonging to an ogre. He took her to his big black tent and chucked her in. He'd gobble her up later.

She sat in the dark and wept bitter tears. Weren't things supposed to get easier? Isn't that how the stories went? She sat for a long time into the dark until a voice—a quiet voice—said:

"Look up and become a Raven."

She looked up and saw, hanging from the roof of the tent, many animal skins. There was a cloak made entirely of raven feathers. Having nothing else to go on but the still, small voice, she tried on the cloak.

For a long time she tried to make the raven cloak fit but it just didn't. She felt despondent. *I can't even trust the still, small voice?*

As she turned this thought round and around, she noticed the pelt of a fox, glowing red in the dark. She reached up, pulled it down and tried it on. It fit perfectly. Immediately her nostrils twitched. She could feel the scent of a breeze. She crouched on the dirt and started to dig down. Soon her hands had dug under the felt of the tent and the breeze had got stronger. She made a tunnel and dug her foxy way out. As raven she would have been banging on the roof forever.

She ran and she ran and she ran. Back to the place her mother and father lived, next to a great lake surrounded by larch. She was back at her lake. When she came to the water she bent down to drink.

This is what the lake showed her.

What she saw was not a woman with a fox pelt on, she saw a fox.
She had become fox.

At that exact moment her father, out on the lake on his kayak, spotted the fox on the beach. He quietly paddled up and got out onto the sand. He walked towards his daughter with salmon in one hand and a net in the other. She pushed all her energy into her eyes for him to recognize her, but how could he?

He would offer her the salmon and she would leap for it as he hurled the net. She would withdraw, then circle again for the salmon.

All afternoon the dance went on. And behind them: father behind father behind father, daughter behind daughter behind daughter.

Suddenly, for no reason we know of, the father softened, put his net down and threw the salmon to his daughter who is a fox. He turned and drew his kayak further up onto the beach.

She gobbled the fish, then turned and ran fast towards her parents' tent. If she could just get home then maybe everything would fix itself.

It is dusk now. Torches are lit in the village as she ducks through the villagers' legs to get to the tent—she can see the wooden door and the tightly bound felt and her heart is drum thumping in her ribs, under her flickering fire fur.

She is running into the tent and just as she gets to the door—

WHAM

The hinge of the door, the whole tent, shifts on itself. Her nose smacks the wooden frame and blood drips onto snow. She shakes herself down, withdraws, and tries again.

WHAM

It is hard when a home turns on you.

Four times the tent twists and refuses her. By now it is almost dark and the people are watching. She is hurting, fox woman is hurting, and she knows she cannot go home again. At least not in any way she would have understood back in the hut by the forest.

In her flickering fire fur heart she makes a decision.

She shoots between the people's legs, twists away from their grasping hands and hurtles from the village. Past the moon rising lake, through crunchy grasses, and over streams she is running, through stands of pale larch and little hills becoming mountains, and she is gasping and rattling and sparking and running and every time she puts a paw on the soil another star bursts into the heavens a great crest of them above her wrought in a patterning so beautiful we can barely speak of it and she is running and now she is leaping and now she is singing her song for the moon and there is skip sometimes in her bounds—every time she puts a paw on the soil new shoots sprout and as I hear it she is a great thought of the earth a great trail of brushfire and exquisite aloneness and as far as I know

> she is running
> > running
> > > to this day
> she is running

✳✳✳

And they push out together on the waves, where the sweet river water meets the salt of the sea, and the man looks over and shouts over the green-dipped churn:

"And what did you learn?"

Kiddo replies, "I learnt that women should marry who they want and only if they want, that a tongue can carry a story as cutting as a blade, and that such a blade can break enchantments, that sometimes we make a big hullabaloo of leaving and then things get worse! And that sometimes a fox sees her reflection in the deep water and she can never go home again. That's what I learnt, Dad.

Ask me again in an hour, and I'll have something different."

Chapter Two

Man on Raft, Talking to Himself

And as she sleeps he talks to himself, that old abiding friendship.

In a brownstone in New York City, he once dreamt that a fairy tale was a kind of breast milk from the earth to us humans. A song-line that pours troublesome nutrition into our pretending-to-be-modern hearts.

So all day long he thinks about this.

That afternoon in Brooklyn it rains so hard you can barely walk upright, so he shelters in the doorway of a dive bar scrawling what he just thought on a napkin. The rain seems to banish a lot of static, and for a few hours he gets just a glimpse of the spirits secreted in lively Iranian hand gestures, sees little furry faces furtively peer up from under a rain mac as Jenny scuttles for the bus.

Just a few miles away, something like the Iliad is erupting within the power squabbles of Wall Street, and a distant relative of Beowulf is wandering Central Park looking for his Grendel.

He watches with his peregrine eyes; seeing knights in panther skin erupt from the subway speaking swiftly in a kind of bardic hip-hop, he spies pummelling battles of seething love almost on the scale of Tristan and Isolde taking place at low volume and high intensity in the dark corner of the coffee shop. You'd have to be mad not to see it. It's not whole stories he's beholding but moments, images, something of a frenetic jumble. Not quite a myth, but mythic. Hints really. We have the image but not the narrative. For a myth you'd need a more sophisticated pattern. Something you could build on. Not a leap but a bridge. For a myth you need something more than an entirely human point of view.

As humans we're not living myth, we're living myths. Plural. They compete. There are differing stories constantly trying to be told through us, different temples that seek our libation. That send us crazy till we blurt them out. There are perspectives in us that aren't even human; there are thoughts that swoop wonkily through with the bright flashes of a jungle bird, or are preserved perfectly in peat until we are ready to be thought by them.

Some thinking is very patient. It will wait years for us to catch up.

But the hour is getting late now. And when the stories we tell only have a human directive peering back at us we start to get very lost. We hypnotise ourselves with our own gaze. In such a moment it is quite possible to bury your heart under a rock and quite forget where you put it.

But he means what he says: some of the rough gods are still amongst us—and not just the porcelain ones that look a little like us on a good day, but the big bad bunch—the raggle-taggle, rhino-tusked menagerie of *the Original Ensemble, the Other Folk, the Gentry, the Benji.* He knows you've glimpsed them, once or twice. They're about.

They are gnawing on the edge of these sentences.

The Otherworld is this one, when it chooses.

It's a convenience to believe that the Old Gods are leaving. Gives us permission for all kinds of nonsense. That they are sitting in the departure lounge of Heathrow and LAX with hurt feelings, waving old bones about and shaking their heads. Clambering into some metaphysical elevator that's going to deposit them in a nursing home for Abandoned Primordials on the other side of Pluto.

We have to stop saying that they die if we stop thinking about them. That's a degraded idea.

Yet that's what so many claim mythology is—us thinking these beings up.

But what if they were allowing us to think them? What if we were getting thought?

Not as manikin puppets, but as part of a profound conversation we can barely remember the moves for anymore.

If they are fled, we can indulge sentimental feelings about them and not worry a jot about crafting a life beautiful and unexpected enough to make them purr.

If they are fled, then we can start to feel sorry for them. That's very foolish.

If they are fled, we can't remember which temple we serve in anymore. And we're all serving something.

One of the canoes they love to travel in is myth. One of the runways they land on is the tongue of the storyteller. That could be you.

Let no one tell you that the old stories don't work our bones over. That all we have is bled out photocopies and cheques that the soul can't cash. Whilst that's occasionally the case, it's by no means the rule. Take courage.

Magic is simply messier and more agile than that kind of morose timeline. We can't be telling our kids that.

Trust the bone house of your own body in this regard. When you flush, wince, shriek and swell your heart to a tale well told, there is torchlight on the wall of Chauvet Cave. It's a form of cruelty to the story to suggest otherwise.

But friend, you have to know that the old stories come with consequence. They will ask they will ask they will ask something of you. They will ask you to change your life.

They are talking to our left brain, right brain, serpent brain, gorilla brain, elegant-cloud-over-moisty-hills brain, old brain, new brain, skeptical brain, exhausted parent brain, terrified brain, celibate brain, horny brain, hands extended into the nourishing dark that hangs over a late summer cornfield brain, strategic brain, hang-it-all please god almighty let me taste real love one last time before they throw me in the clay brain. All the brains.

He repeats: the gods haven't fled, they're not sulking, but they do want your full attention.

At the time he first thought this he was flying over Northern Canada. Still six hours till he landed in San Francisco. Below him all the Sigurds and Bjorns were wiping the salt from their beards half lunatic from the wind moving through the churn of ten centuries ago. They row and sing and die and live. Everything is beneath the plane. All the Vikings, the Dutch, English, Spaniards, all heading to the New World, which is the Otherworld. All centuries were below them, flapping open like a barn door in a hurricane.

In the next week he would talk about the books he writes and meet many hundreds of people. He would try and ignore the fairy tales lurking behind their conversations, try to be accommodating to the ravenous look in Terry from Detroit's eyes, and a hurried attempt to push the sleeve of a paisley shirt over what is clearly a paw clutching a pen. Up there on Olympus he half watched a movie from which he couldn't hear the sound, just a lot of mouthing. He likes looking at the concerned expressions that dart around on the faces of the characters. He'd hate to hear the script. He thinks how much of his life has been like this—watching the energy of people and how out of tune the sound that sometimes comes out of their mouths is—how out of step with what's actually happening. Maybe this is how we seem to the gods now: that one day one of them gently reached over and turned down the volume.

Maybe it's not that we can't hear the gods but that they can't hear us.

Chapter Three

Shameless

"We are all scandals."
James Hillman

Swish Swish Swish

He awakes to the movement of waves, not river currents, and the scent of roasting coffee. Little accomplice is fixing herself some breakfast.

Her moon-beautiful face is all to itself today. She has countless acres of thought inside herself these days. She's changing, deepening, growing. He loves her more than all of Persia.

He glances out the side of their ramshackle craft. Is that the green Aegean? Nope, it's the English channel. He can see a bloody ferry.

He looks down at the papers he's brought with him. Nutty little poems mostly, and notes he wrote to himself. The notes are to do with words rarely mentioned, or maybe even expected of men anymore:

Decency, upstandingness, courage under fire, tenacity, sustained generosity.

God almighty, are these words even a comprehendible currency anymore? He's started to see his child's face flinch when yet another man is marched in front of the news for groping a girl of roughly an age where he should be paying for her school fees. She's getting a very specific message about the masculine every day now. That tunes out a hundred other signals.

This is our deserved ruin. But he believes in those words.
Knows men of such calibre.

Fuck. What happened to us? *Arthur? Robin? Crazy Horse?*

"And David saw an enemy on every hill."

Is Finn MacColl just a creep with a propensity for random acts of violence, who scrawls down some lyric poetry on the side to feel better? Is Genghis just some sadist dragging his cock like a ploughshare from one side of Asia to another? Was it always this degraded?

We've established the man on the raft is in heartbreak. That something so utterly fundamental has passed through him he's forever changed, that has so mangled, contorted then flayed alive his sensibilities, has been so beyond his capacity to shape or control or even negotiate, that he is left with a grinding hollowness, a prairie wide emptiness he suspects he will never come back from.

And if he can't come back from it, he has elected to talk to it. And It's the one thing he can't find a single soul to talk about it with.

Oh, he could growl on about sodomy till he's blue in the face, or yet more witheringly conditional, ever-whittled-down expectations of relationships, holding boundaries, or "me" time. He could talk about cutting the ties that bind, or taking the road less travelled, or where to meet women of an appropriate age without risk of upsetting almost anybody, anywhere. In the absence of religion, up pops psychology to plump up the god of ourselves.

We expect so little from men now, it's quite ok to shuffle from one loveless hump after another. A time where more could be expected seems ludicrous. Pitifully unaware. Men simply don't have the stuff. It's a horrible kind of victory to a damaged masculinity that no one seems to have noticed yet.

And let's say it.

He's an animal too. An irritable menagerie, a silverback, a coyote who covers his tracks by pissing in the dust, a cannibal with cologne, a smash-bash-crash of libidinous impulse who would like to punch in the face every second person he met, just to see what happened. He's just a fraction of a second away from everyone he sees scuttling off to rehab. Of course he is.

But the point is, he knows it. And he's known it for over forty years. And on occasion he's negotiated terms for parole, even broken out the zoo for an hour or two.

He knows it. He knows exactly what this endless polyrhythmic hallucination feels like to negotiate. This exhausting, often degraded attempt to maintain the shape of being a man.

But this kind of love conjured something else in him. And this will-not-will not-will not be made smaller, or more convenient, or dragged into the milky sedative of appropriate forgetting. This is a mystery.

He doesn't need more applause, tantric massage techniques, or a creel of women.

He just needs someone to speak to him in his old names.

He takes out his first little poem. These notes have stayed buried in a drawer for a long time.

The receiver of the goods is long flown and the line is dead. The phone wire is cut. So he gives them, as he must, to the milky trail of foam behind the boat. The very milk of Aphrodite's breast.

My vineyards are in bloom my darling my vineyards are in bloom.

awake north wind
come south wind in your fullness
blow on the perfume of my garden
that it may spread abroad
and let my lover come
come to my
generous acres
and taste its choicest fruits.

He drops it into the squall, and sees it immediately disappear. Gobbled up.
He peers about.

Where are you love? I saw you once, and swallowed all the ruin that such a debt requires. Seeing you struck dumb all other voices in me but the truest.

I'm not sure what I was thinking. I wasn't thinking.

What am I doing on this fucking raft?

Chapter Four

Island of the Locked-in Secret

And they came to a Lonely Island.

It's a tiny rock, just a few miles from the Devon coast. Agh. Dad bangs the side of the raft and croons his plea to the timber that they should get south. The wood creaks and groans, "All in good time". The girl surveys, and spies a woman on the distant beach, seemingly talking to the wind. It's odd, the woman is walking but keeps her head down, like she has been caught stealing something. There are others wandering, but they all seem oblivious to each other, ashamed in some fashion, like they've just staggered out of a courtroom.

The girl keeps looking but speaks quietly like Odysseus out of the corner of her mouth to Dad:

"Will these people be savage or kind?"

This is The Island of the Locked-in Secret.

Whole decades get snarled up here, tongues get salted and made mute here, our hopeful little tug boat roped tight in the harbour of our unsaid life. No real journey can avoid visiting this bay.

Some quadrant or particle or fragment of our soul abides here. No one is excused this station.

For the first time and absolutely not the last time, the man starts to wonder in which dimension is this journey unfolding? Inner or outer? It is growingly more ludicrous to make such distinction.

And what are they witnessing? Dad and daughter have stumbled into the scene of some ramshackle old play. They wiggle their ears like hares and settle, a good audience. Collect your programme and ice cream. Come Greek tragedy, Come Pan, lord of theatre critics. He's here, tucked away in the beach grasses, thin, clear flute music, unspeakably lovely. Delicate for such a hair-backed wild one.

The girl is right: there are words moving from the woman to the wind.

But more unexpectedly, there are words moving *back*. There was a time when such conversations were an eruptive magic, a trafficking across species, as dynamic as repentance, a troublesome runway with which the gods could swoop down and walk with us in the cool of the day. When conversation flared up between a child and the marvellous world: debates, sorrows, remonstrations, humblings, cosmic finger-wagging and delicate praise delivered by the wind.

And, as the two of them watch, such a wind is doing something just like that, to a woman all caught in on herself. The wind is reminding her of another night, thirty years before. A spring evening when she made love with a man that was not her husband. A man called Elias.

The wind speaks quietly to her, "You forget I'm *old*, Heather. Vast. I was there."

Heather keeps looking forward, towards yellow bumps of gathered sand and grass. She's vague, "I can't remember."

"Oh come. They say you were never so wild again. That later you took his hand and walked down into the valley full of daffodils. Your hips felt loose and womanly, red soil under bare feet. Everything still but the mad pony of your blood.

Nothing like a daffodil in the moonlight Heather. Like a bolt of sun, a yolk.

Made you cry because you knew this time would be so short. This wilding. But it's in your heart today, Heather, I can hear its drum thump. I think you saw something out there. Under the moon. One of the Old Women. The ones that walked over my northern snowy hump, back and forth between lands, long ago.

One of those who remind you of the old arrangement. That on the night a child is born, there is another one that comes, a twin. A wild one that is banished. Shameless, regal and utterly alive. You got reminded that night, didn't you?"

The wind touches her chest, gently.

"That's pure living Heather. You never lose the scent.

It marked you, didn't it? After? Your friends? They saw something but they didn't know what it was. So they make it cheap. Made them sour, your joy.

It's not your story Heather. Shrug it off.
You just got touched by one of the old powers.

That night you were ablaze in your naturalness.
Like a waterfall. Like a roving deer.

They should be kissing the hem of your skirt girl.
We all did y' know, for thousands of years we did."

And now Heather lowers her head. "I lied. I lied and I lied and I lied. Ever since.
Can't remember much else. And not even good lies. No real purpose to them. Not
powerful ones, no juice in them. No one got saved by lying. Just slow culling. Of
me and whatever I thought I stood for. Pretending I didn't see it.

I've seen her. I saw her. God almighty I saw her.

She stood by a stream, her feet just a few inches off the ground. And me with his
sap between my legs.

I thought the waters had a huge golden coin in it, big as a shield, but when I looked
again it was the reflection of the moon above her head.

She told me a far-away-story.
But a story that I knew. I knew it.

I saw truth and I let it wither. I starved it out. I never gave it oxygen.
It was my moment. There hasn't been another. I saw something impossible.

That alone was enough. I never missed Elias and I didn't feel guilty. It's her out
there what I betrayed. And the baby that I gave away. And I have walked this beach
alone ever since.

Never forgot it though. The baby or the feeling. She put something in me. In the
spring time I want to rut. I come alive, like the doe in the dew. Take the royal sap.
Boxing off suitors till the buck comes. The bull-wolf. Leader. Animal thing in me.
It's like a hurt between my legs. A craziness.

When it claims me I'm not a mother or a wife. I'm a breeder. Hot time. Long-
shanked. Alive in the byre. The rut in the broom.

God almighty it's wondrous. I see the moon glowing in the water and I has to go. I
has to go. I've seen it pass like a virus through the towns of the far west when spring
comes. In villages and hamlets and out in the stubbled fields: sweat and heat and
magic. The ancient, wild dance.

She wanted me to claim that for myself. To wear it like a scarlet cloak, not bury it away. She made it holy. She made my desire holy. There's no place for it. Whore. That's what they think.

So I strangle magic."

And the wind spoke, "The door to the marvellous is still open. Say it. It's a betrayal not to tell a story you've been given."

"If I tell this story I will not be loved."

"You can't love everyone."

As if fighting to wake from a dream, or breaking a long rooted enchantment, Heather stops walking, shaking her head. "This is the story I saw in the surface of the stream. This is it.

In the golden coin of the moon. This is my red bead language. I want to tell you a fairy story. This is the only way I can tell you."

✳✳✳

Tatterhood

Pines surround the tower, the moat, the ancient seat.

In the snowy north, on a runic scatter of hill and fjord lives a good Queen. A good King. No Herods dangling their cherubs, but rivers to their people. Soul-broad. All the right villains are chucked into their chilly dungeons.

And above, in the great hall golden coin falls into the welcome hats of the musicians. These sovereigns can conjure heaven, but will plough a furrow with their very fists, if the gods dictate. Their bustling cosmos holds the crouching weaver, the herder, the raw-knuckled fisher people tight in the blue kingdom. All the sheep are gathered in.

But no child.

They are plump with their role, joyous on the royal lanes, but the belly is crow-bare. The leap of the mountain hare is crippled by the scythe. A scattering of pain webs the ceiling of these lovers.

The midnight hump becomes dreadful. The King withers and wipes his shame on the tapestry. Their grief moves steadily out to meet the land. Trout turn in the bruise-black streams and spurt flaccid eggs on the river bank. The blond corn loses shape, rots into murk. The fox shudders with orange fire as it starves.

Someone good meaning offers delicate suggestion; why not take a niece for the house? To flower the corridors with laughing, to loosen the slow tune of the death fiddle. The sovereigns listen from beneath their wet bundle of sorrow and do indeed call such a girl to their service.

The vastness of the castle is hers. The kitchens, the chapel, the sounding-halls where poetic champions draw from the scarred valleys of language. Deerhounds her companion, trotting the gloom. A goodly trouble, she cracks black ice simply by her kid-swagger, her games, her lovely, raucous sounds.

She is gifted a ball. A golden ball. Early in the day she likes to take the ball out to the very edges of the garden. Where a crusting of forest waits. Where prim hedges meet the energy of twig and spell. She loves that place.

It is there she takes her ball, luminous, an axis-mundi. She plays all day, cattle-tracks of concentration on her brow, waiting for the dusking time, the mottling light.

Of a sudden, a girl steps forward.

Clear gypsy—tilt of head, a-swathed with feather, mucky footed, delirious and forested.

That golden ball
starts to leap between the two.

From the trimmed grasses to the murk and back again.

A throw like a sighing tide. Further back in the tree line something watches.

The niece runs to the sovereigns,

"I have news!
I have met a leafy-girl
who says her granny
can make bellies swell
like a browning loaf:

She sings salt back to the ocean
she calls the owl to nestle in the lonely croft
of your hips."

They are summoned.

And the dark stick behind our young one emerges.

Hawk-nosed, thistle-haired, spark-eyed, yolk-fat with cobra-knowledge, pockets
a-clatter with magics, brown fingers dragging rooster blood from the heart of the
moon. In the grandeur of the hall, at first she denies the powers. That the child is
tongue-eager, bent to exaggeration. But as the dusk shadows flood over the gold,
she relaxes. In that time before candles are lit, she shows some form. Her proud
shape juts into the room.

She is:

mearcstapa - *the boundary walker*
zaunreiter - *a hedge straddler*
hagazussa - *hag*

She gulps brandy and spits chicken-claw words:

"You will never grow large. Your bed is too high, too smart, too far from dirt.

In your far off tower, a woman's eggs grow dizzy, a man's pearling will be as a drizzle
of stagnant water.

You can rut like the creamy whale ablaze with its concubine in the indigo kingdom,
but nothing much will happen.

Take your bed, your pillows that hold your thinking, your graceful sheets out to
the furthest stable with the pitted earth floor. Tonight, woman, after you bathe,
carry the water, a-clink down the stairs, sloshing with your filth. Give it to the
stable dirt: four-directioned, intended, deliberate. Then drag the bed over the pool
and start the steady grind of your seeding.

At dawn
push the bed aside.

There will be two flowers—

white and red.
Eat the white.

Under no circumstances eat the red.

Do this and all will change."

Her speaking is strange. Like words gathered from underneath a stone. By now the hall is almost completely dark.

As the page lights the first candle, the women canter out on the dark horses of their pride.

✳✳✳

Morning casts golden light through the stable beams. Bees make rough speech in the furry meadows. The great bed is pulled aside and there they are. The white flower eager for the rays, the red flower sullen, hung-over, drunk on privacy. No one can stop the Queen. She squats, all fours, like a heated bitch, and snaffles up the red.

"My hands made me do it!" comes from the roughed gob, her tongue still greedily circling her mouth.

Now, the nerves come. She plucks the white with more canny deliberation, calls her husband as witness and waits.

✳✳✳

In a high tower, nine months have passed. Ladies jostle to call the secrets to the ear that a woman needs when she sweats the red gate between worlds. As a slurry of blood shimmers her thighs, all hold the image strong of the babe in health: pink toed, blue eyed, cornrow fingers. Keep thinking it into being.

What bursts through
is not that.

A small goat
hoofs towards the light.
Red-cowled, sticky furred.

A goat.

And riding its greasy back
is a tiny, hairy baby girl.

A tattered hood
shields most of its face,
hanging limply and dripping.

This deviant, this shape-leaper,
this terror-nymph,
waves a wooden spoon
and gallops the stage,
relishing the screams.

She is appetite; desirous,
hungry for taste, hungry for meat.

She speaks:

"Be patient. Another comes. Twins."

A second later, another gush and a radiance arrives—a fat sun after horror night. A
girl, beautiful and bawling, cow lashes, grip firm on the tit. Dawn breaks through
the window. The hairy twin settles in its warmth, beds down on gathered hay.

And all wonder—

"What to do? What to do?"

Plans besieged the twins as they grew. To rupture the love between the two sisters.
But wherever they tried to hide the furry one, whatever far distant attic was her
nest—her sister would find her. Energy moves like fast water between them. As
time bangs on, the castle finds a strange accord with the great awakener.

Her braying intelligence coughs new stories into the midst of the court. She spills
tales of Moroccan silver, and Irish gossip onto the feasting table and all know they
are the wiser for it.

As the second daughter's body starts to bud, to lift toward woman, winter settles
the land with its great flakes of white. There is to be a feast—the first for the fair

daughter to emerge; curved and available. Fresh rushes are laid, thick yellow wicks bright the dark corridors.

The father sits alone on the big seat and runs the sharpener against his loyal blade, mind cloudy with worry.

The cluck-strut and stale language of young suitors is a wearied cloak.

It's Christmas Eve.

When all are settled at table, cup lifted, honeyed chop on plate, a groan comes from outside the hall. A keening of many terrible things. From the tree line, and beyond that the lochs and mountain—

Come Witch.
Come Giant.
Come Ogre.

The gaggle-swarm churn up the frosted turf, defecate on the frozen moat, hurling old, black language at the loafing warriors. Horse-leather drums thump the occult pace, skulls of snow-eagles shake a-top rowan staffs. The butchers cower at table.

But the Tattered sister charges the un-killable throng.

No one blocks her path.

She is swift with the death screech of the owl.

Fists rain-daggers, her fame a slurry of violence, hot landed on ghoulish heads. Adrift in this fury that has greeted them—this tiny sister, this speck of joyous iron, a grand-general of malice—the coven scatters, loses its mighty shape and starts a boozy retreat.

They seem impressed.

Leaning from a window is the bright sister. Spotted—a witch leans from a foaming mare and twists her head clean off. From her crane-skin bag she wrestles a calf's head onto the twitching body but takes her face as booty, blood mad under the braying moon.

✳✳✳

This mid-winter surgery has been a success. The bewildered calf's head squats rough on the lime white body. The chambers ring shrill with a mother's terror; father grips the confirming walls.

Tatterhood is calm:

"This shape-leap
offers relief.
Rather an animal power close by,
than the violence of unready love
that was being prepared.

As it goes, I have the sight.
I know where her head will go.

But two lochs north
there is a longhouse
of Hags.

The head will be placed on a
rusty nail.

Me and my calf-sister
will take the foray.

We will collect,
and with heavy penalty."

The King offers a hundred horseman, a thousand archers, witch-killers, holy sprinklers, coal-souled mercenaries. Beserkers.

The sisters will take none of it but a ship.

The crow caws that this is for them alone.

✳✳✳

One loch then the other. The nested croft of the Blaggard Hags. The harvest is smooth as the Goat-Sister threshes the flesh wall. The head is scooped delicately from that nail. Placed back on rightful shoulders with three flecks silvering the blond.

Decision on the boat. To turn home or the whale-road?

They settle for the vast unfurling, experience's bounty, to reach jubilation, to hang foamy thinking like animal skins from the smoky mast. Three, four years pass this way.

✳✳✳

A distant port. A King in middle years, widowed—but one who leans into danger. Makes his way through the rigging and gulls to befriend these salty women. His son, with unsung charisma, follows behind.

A love affair erupts between the noble and the fair sister. A horn blows for the marriage binding, but Tatter waves her chafed hand, and chants from the greasy hood:

"Older sisters marry first.
Root me with the son—
a double wedding."

Grief-choked, the son and father debate by the long jetty, quietly turning life's forks in their subtle hands. The older shape crumples at the vastness of his son's panache.

Before long, three horses and a goat take a flowered lane to the simple chapel.

At the back, Tatterhood and the son, her goat's fur stiffened with mud, his horse sure-hoofed, gold bridle and saddle, licked with rubies.

"Why do men never ask the questions that open a woman's soul?" she peers up, curious. "If I tell you what to ask, will you ask me?"
The boy coughs and straightens.

"Certainly."

A true dowry.

"Why do I ride a goat?
Why do I carry a spoon?
Why do I wear a hood?"

"Because for one with eyes to behold it, it's not a goat!"
A Castilian steed rears up.

"Because for one with eyes to behold it, it's not a spoon!"
A rowan wand hums air.

"Because for one with eyes to behold it, it's not a hood!"
A crown of dog rose and antler bone sits aloft.

Bundled hair like dark torrent surges as a keen sea down the small of her back. Foals quiver on the green hill. Brandy is drunk from the gypsy's hand. We hear a pipe, a drum, the rasp of fiddle.

Her beautiful, ordinary face gleams by the chapel's yellow candle.

The wedding will last for years.

※※※

"The wedding will last for years." They puzzle over that for hours on the raft. Was it a mistake, did she mean marriage? She seemed emphatic in her choice of word. They watch Heather for a little while sitting on the beach, absolutely still, like she's porcelain. She seems smaller than when the story moved through her. Then the waters move them on.

The two intrepids take Heather's story and gather round it, each image a warming flame. They throw questions between them like that golden ball:

What does it mean to eat a red flower? To lose your head to the witches?
To know the questions that unlock a woman's heart?

These are immense, formal enquiries, deep as Plato, that stretch an evening just beautifully between a parent and kid, before they fall asleep, tucked up under the furs. All night long they drift and dream, drift and dream.

In his dreams, the mermaid he loves is trapped under ice, under the belly of a great, dark shark.

Chapter Five

My Heart was Broken the Moment I Set Eyes on You

*"Such longing for love, rolling under my heart
pouring so much mist over my eyes."*
Archilochus

*We have entered the Garden through
the lost and lonely gate.*

His mind is a machete, and each morning it hacks through the sorrowing grasses to make a path to his sweetheart's door. At five years old he had heard her name secreted in a piece of music his parents played as they had their supper. As the magical black circle spun restlessly on the record player, he lay helpless and curled in the sound at the top of the stairs. So there is just one, after all, in the end.

It's a terrible thing, those moments between waking and opening your eyes. The body has not yet constructed the necessary fictions required to make living without her tolerable, or ok. There's just a moment of terrible, animal awareness, like falling high off a swing as a child, a terrible hoof to the guts as you fall towards pain.

But for a moment, he keeps those eyes clamped shut.

Can an Aphrodite moment *include* ruin? Is it ok that seaweed-tasting whisky is a medicinal hammer to shuffle oneself through the cramped and breathless umbilical cord of broken sleep between one day and a stumbling, zombied next? What's her counsel about loss? Or the kind of despair that creeps so pervasively through a house it becomes its roof, walls and floor. It would appear it is there we have entered the care of Saturn.

Maybe the two of them have an arrangement: Aphrodite lures you in and then ships you off to the king of limits, frustration, and hopelessness. So where is the gradient between our two teachers? Where does the fulsome breast of golden milk become the granite wall of Saturn's terrible attention?

And down in the fucking basement, Hephaistos—husband of Aphrodite, cuckold, cripple and blacksmith to the gods—bang bang bangs on the blistering machinery of our quivering, whimpering baby-hearts. We flame up in his ancient hands, then are shoved down into the steaming waters of our undoing. We flay around, stupid innocents of the world, wringing our hands as he growls, "Too late bitch, too late." The poets will claim he's tempering your soul down there, making robust your shape, but everyone else knows he's tearing you a new arsehole. It's what love does. One does not discount the other.

For a moment, the man keeps his eyes shut.

These are words we put in the deep freeze:
bereft, despair, abandoned.

Last night, even the crows left my roof.

I am not too sophisticated to be shattered,
not too swarthy to be felled at the knee,

Not such a king that I will not rush
into black night when I hear the
cry of the Heavenly Woman
from the lost and lonely rushes.

⁂

But a day at sea can be nothing if not changeable.

And thankfully it's different for the girl. Misery guts over there can button it for five minutes. Isn't it grand to be woken by music? And no grey, computerised thump, but the gleeful, scratchy sound of fiddle and concertina, a clarinet somewhere in the back. She opens her eyes and rubs, and sees the marvellous approaching them.

The morning music is coming from another craft, it's a bobbing bird-house of sound, a boat full of miscellaneous mischief and elaborate heartbreak. There are delegations from the old houses of Eastern Europe on board, even Russia. There are exiled royals from a hundred years ago, rubbing furs with an old woman fixing a television with a knitting needle and a Swiss army knife. There are sable pelts and horse shoes, gold teeth in wide handsome smiles and, of course, a cauldron of beet soup burbling away in the background.

The music quietens but does not stop. How could it ever stop? Crows would fall dead from their branches. The inhabitants call over, with the traditional question of all of us trying to get home:

"Hey there! Are you savage or are you kind?"

Dad and daughter call back excitedly, "We are kind! Your kind!"

"They didn't say that at Dover. They had no story to tell us, no hospitality, none. We've been visiting your country for hundreds of years and now we are strangers?"

On the raft, the two brood, disconsolate. It is a physical pain to hear such things. Then the girl pipes up, "I have stories! And we know small, deserted coves to bring your boat up on, throw a rope!"

So the two crafts pull close, barely a lick of foam between them. Now we can see more faces, and furry critters we barely have a name for. And for an hour, more or less, the girl of the raft cries welcome, warms their weary bones with West Country stories of *The Mid-Wife and the Fairy, The Grey Wether Stones, The Voyage of Brutus,* till they have had stories with an address on them, that circulate just miles from shore. Maybe the coast they peer out at is now a little storied, a little populated, a little nuanced.

An old man from the back of the boat calls out. He is old Yevgeny.

"Like for like! That was some sweetness you sent. We will send you stories back. Why on earth are you out here anyway, on these ragged seas?"

The girl shouts, "We are sailing to Arcadia! We have some questions for Aphrodite, concerning love!" Her father shudders.

The wind curls the reply straight into the ears of the travellers, and they smile amongst themselves understandingly. The old man is helped to the front of their creaking craft, so he is only a foot or so away from the travellers.

"We will be generous with our stories! But love is a word of breadth and depth. I will tell you a loving story about my teacher. It may not be the exact face of love you seek, but tell it I will. May crumbs of good plum cake fall from it and into your mouths. We give you two stories back."

✳✳✳

The Holy Couple

The Baal Shem Tov gathered his inner circle of disciples together, "Next Sabbath I'm going to show you what Sabbath really is." A great excitement moved through them, and they prepared with highest care—bathing themselves in the mikveh, the ritual pool, changing into their special clothes, and turning up extra early at Synagogue.

To their disappointment, they didn't notice anything particular auspicious, just a very plain-looking Jewish man at the back praying with delight and joy. Pssch. Hardly a burning bush. They felt let down. But, afterwards, the Baal Shem Tov gathered his disciples in his study where they could peer down on the ramshackle little house that the poor man lived in. The little man entered.

"Good Shabbos, my sweet wife," he said, joyously.

"And a restful and holy Shabbos to you, my dearest husband," his wife responded. A moment or two later, the gathered students heard the husband and wife singing "Shalom Aleichem" together, the words moving out gladly into the dark. When they had finished, the husband said to his wife, "Sweetheart, let us make Kiddush".

But such was their poverty they had no money for wine. So the wife placed two tiny rolls on the table and they made Kiddush over them. Then the wife spoke, "And for the fish course, I have something very special." She stood and brought a small platter of beans to the Shabbos table.

They made prayer, ate a spoonful of their humble repast, and their faces shone with delight. The poor man sang some of the old songs and then it was time for the soup course. They took another spoon of beans and smiled at each other. "Umm, what a wonderful Shabbos soup," they remarked.

They took a third spoonful in the place of the meat, and the fourth the dessert.

In great merriment, the poor man spoke, "Come my sweetest one, let us dance to celebrate the holy Shabbos". And so they both got up and began to dance about their Shabbos table, laughing and laughing with joy.

At that moment, in the dark of the study, each of the disciples felt an immense happiness rise within their hearts.

The Baal Shem Tov whispered:

"You are experiencing Sabbath's joy, so close to the joy this holy couple are experiencing. You should know that it was not simple food they tasted, but the Sabbath itself."

And so it was.

***

And Yevgeny called out to his god, "Is that not a love story?"

The man on the raft quietly wept.

By now, the others are trading food between boats, great trails of sausages, lumps of cheese, apples, tangerines, a little dark chocolate, a bottle or two. And the old woman has fixed the television! It lurches into life for just a little while, *Zorba the Greek* crackles away as they toast old Anthony Quinn and dream of warmer waters.

That night, the old man visits the raft to speak more of his old spiritual teacher.

"Yisrael Ben Eliezer was a dreamy boy, a sensitive, who wandered out past the village into the fields and dark forests of the wild Carpathian mountains, alive to rivers and birds and god's murmurs. And he loved to reply to the whispers, some liveliness gave him the belief that the holy one delighted to hear his talk. We see him, weaving through the long grasses, and jumping the green stream, held aloft by his creator, the boy luminous with their gentle discourse.

His wingspan was wide: he worked as a caretaker in the synagogue, a labourer and a ritual slaughterer of animals, but he quietly became a diligent student of the Torah and a learned Kabbalist. A kind of saint in disguise, his nature wanderings made him highly skilled with herbal medicine, and, combined with prophetic ability and healing power, quickly made him very well known indeed.

But he wore his erudition most humbly, and he and his wife, Rebbetzyn Sarah took the observance of mitzvah—of hospitality to guests—so seriously they would employ villagers to wait on the lonely rutted tracks outside their settlement to welcome lonely travellers to their home."

"Was he magical?" asks the girl.

The old man positively twinkles in the lantern light.

"Oh yes. Baal Shem Tov literally means, 'Master of the Good Name'. So let us all humbly strive to be mistresses and masters of a good name. Baal Shem derives from a Maker of Amulets, which adds another thought again—his amulets actually worked.

And who can forget naughty Alexei, his wagon driver (who often accompanied the Rabbi on his mysterious and magical trips), who would sip schnapps under a blanket, then snooze as the horse and sled appeared to fly through the air, so great was the distance travelled. Maybe his sled is a little like your raft. Humble, but taking you many miles."

The old man gathers to go now, but he leans towards the girl.

"Deep inside you, a poor man and his wife dance around the Sabbath table, their faces shining with the wealth that cannot be counted. There are two levels in the study of the Torah: Torah of the mind and Torah of the heart. The mind ponders, comprehends, and understands; the heart feels. The Baal came to reveal Torah as it effects the heart as well."

He smiles again, and clambers back to his craft. In their travels they will hear stories of such grandeur they will be speechless and sometimes ecstatic, but they will never shake off the story of the poor man and his wife. It will be with them forever.

In the morning, they hear the strains of wedding tunes coming from the boat, and this time it is not an old man but old woman who totters into their raft, squeezing and tutting about the lack of space for the largeness of tale she has. She is old Rosa.

And she has a tale of Vasya Whitefeet himself, gypsy lover supreme. *Go man, go!*

✳✳✳

Vasya Whitefeet

There was, there was, there was: a wealthy gypsy gifted almost beyond measure. He had mastery of the forest, the pastures and the villages. He had only one son, Vasya. And why Whitefeet? Because, unlike his dark-skinned friends, he was born as white as snow, as white as a swan's wing, as white as ivory, as white as Elizabethan silk.

On his father's death the boy was twenty, and inherited a huge fortune. He had it all, but he felt he had nothing. It gnawed at him, this feeling, itched his bones inside his skin. So Whitefeet decided to find out about life, learn a craft, have a look-see at how the wider world ticked. He changed into scruffy and threadbare clothes, took two coins, a leaky oilskin, a stale crust of bread and headed out on the road.

Here I come!
Spinning my Wheel of Fire!
I am a Wolf King
Disguised as a mutt

Quickly, within a mile, he came to a healthy looking gypsy camp: handsome tents, women singing, men arguing, many horses, many chickens, the fire in keen excitement. Along his way he had smeared mud to hide his complexion, and acted the fool on arrival. They allowed him to loiter under his funky oilskin, mainly to blame him for camp misfortune or to rip into him for humour's sake.

One evening, as dusk was falling, music was starting up around the fire as it did every night. There was a guitar slinger and accordion player. Whitefeet asked for a play on the accordion.

"You Vasenka? Can you play a note? People will laugh if you can't," said the accordionist.

"Don't know unless I try," he gurgled, scratching his head. The amused player handed over his instrument, whilst winking at the others. This should be good. Idiot.

But it was good. It was incandescent. It was stupendous.

Whitefeet prowled round the fire, crouching low then standing on one leg like a heron, then leaping 'cross the flames, his fingers scattering lightning trills over the buttons, hurling so much power into the sultry night that the gypsies were soon tapping their feet and waving their hats with joy. He was a wonder! A proper hustler, he then retreated immediately under the oilskin to let them speculate about him in his absence. *To let them miss him.*

From then on, every night they coaxed him out from under his oilskin, his earth mattress and knackered boots for pillow, "Play Vasya, play!" And play he did, ablaze, nothing short of a firebird, a strutting idiot-genius, as all swayed dreamily and clucked about his gifts. And he may still be there today, but for what happened next.

The old woman checks on the rapt attentiveness of her two listeners on the raft, bustles her blanket tighter, and continues:

A rumour came to camp, stronger than a rumour, a straight up fact that the gorgeous Rosa was to be married, to a powerful local man. The arriving fact would then be weighted down with the whisper that beautiful, heart-wrenching Rosa was not in fact enamoured of her future husband. Not at all. And her father didn't care a jot. Wherever this news landed, so did a kind of perfume that sent all the men inward, unusually quiet.

Whitefeet lived for this kind of thing.

Early next morning he crept home. After a long soak in the bath, he gathered his very best duds: his Moroccan boots, brocade shirt, his most powerful horse.

"What's this all about my son?" his mother asked.

(At this the old woman teller on the raft winks, and actually claims to BE his mother. Just a minute before she also claims to be THE Rosa of the tale)

"Staggering Rosa is to be married to a man she does not care for. Maybe I will save her the bother. I will go and see exactly what is what."

His mother countered, "Do as you must my boy, but know that a Gypsy father's word should not be crossed lightly: beware her father."

And Vasya rode, and rode, and rode to the wedding, carrying only his favourite violin, with gold on both his wrists.

When he arrived he started to play the most potent and deliciously sorrowful tunes he knew. Watching from a few feet away, with just the smoke of the fire between them, Rosa gazed at the handsome musician, having arrived from out of nowhere and playing the secret cadence of her own heartstrings. Who was he?

I told you baby
I am the Wolf King
I sail with Jason
I play drums with Cash

So caught up with their boozing and deal-making, no one noticed when the musician stole up to the bride-to-be and whispered in her ear:

"Rosa, my heart was broken the moment I set eyes on you. Braid your life with mine and come away with me. This man is not your true husband."

Rosa was silent, but gave him a look all lovers understand. Undercover of darkness they stole away on his powerful horse.

But all notice when the woman at the centre is missing: the wine becomes brackish, the fireside tunes are nothing but a stone hurled through a window. The energy leaves the gathering. Everything becomes cheap.

The furious father sent one hundred horses out in pursuit, all snorting, all jumping. But there's no catching lovers like that.

Into the rain into the rain into the rain you can't catch them

His mother was waiting, arms open for the young woman.

"Mother! Love her as your own daughter."

Mother agreed, but then cooked up an enormous, utterly flamboyant display of grief on a related matter, made an art of her woe:

"But a wedding for you two! Don't deny me! We must have a proper, enormous, gypsy wedding! Proper Bang! Bang! Dance till dawn."

Rosa and Whitefeet cheered and agreed, and next morning, Vasya stole back to his oilskin, muddy complexion, earth mattress and boots for pillows. As you can well imagine, the camp was practically burning up with news that a brave and skillful Rom had stolen Rosa away from her fated marriage.

"Maybe you know who wrecked the wedding, eh Vasya?" they joked.

He grinned up with his muddy cheeks. "I do, it was me, all me." He was quietly spoken, but glowing in his triumph.

Their laughter floated into the next century it was so long and hearty. He retorted:

"Laugh my friends, have a good giggle. Ho, ho, ho. And when you've finished, dress in your finery and come to the real wedding, my wedding—at a wealthy friend's just a mile away. You'll love it."

He rode on home as they gathered themselves. When scrubbed, he was unrecognisable as the oilskin boy. He was now the lime-white man. He even greeted them at the gate, "Are you the friends of Whitefeet? Welcome!"

They were offered even finer clothes if they wished, polish for boots, foamy hot water for bathing, beard trims, the whole thing.

Later, when they were feasting and the fire blazed, their host stood up and proposed a toast to Vasya:

"*Chivalei,* let us propose a toast to Rosa and Vasya, love's renegades!"

"But where is he?" a few bellowed back. With that, their host strolled over to the musicians and borrowed an accordion. He swayed, he bent, he leapt the fire, all the while creating a music that would make the whole world swoon.

They all knew of a sudden that something impossible had happened: this elegant host was the oilskin boy who sung down the moon in his music. Gypsies adore such impossibilities and all cheered ecstatically and the party rolled magnificently forward for three days and for three unforgettable nights. After such a time, the gypsies left for their own camp, with beautifully fuzzy heads, wine on their lips, and warmth in their hearts.

And Rosa and Vasya alone in the big house. The big, marble, empty house. After a week the silence grated like a dripping tap.

Rosa peered over at Vasya down the long, lonely length of the table. "My love, are your feet tapping like mine, do you feel a restlessness in the blue smoke of your soul for the fire, the stars, the tent life?"

He gazed adoringly at her. "Dear wife. Mindreader. True Rom. I do. My road is your road. Let's get out of here."

And with that, on one horse and of one mind, they left the big life for the humble, sweet one of the gypsy camp, with its floating accordion tunes and guitar slingers and swishing skirts and gold teeth.

And as far as I hear it, they are leading that camp to this day!

Rosa and Vasya
Kickin' it still

***

"Is that not a love story?" calls the old woman over her shoulder as she huffs and puffs back onto the boat.

Slowly, almost imperceptibly, the two crafts part: the boat for the hidden beach, and the raft further out onto the waves, father and daughter living inside the story. *"Who's your favourite Dad?"* For her it's a slam dunk for Rosa. Rock'n'roll Rosa. Absconding from her own wedding, walking away from the wealthy house, reminding Whitefoot about the outdoor life.

Dad is under the oilskin. Dad is breaking his beloved out from the false wedding and turning on his horse to see she has utterly disappeared, Dad has no music to play. He says nothing about any of this.

Our heartbreak is not our kid's business.

Swish   Swish   Swish

PART TWO

Rhiannon
Horse-Blood
the
MAY EVE

Chapter Six

The Queen of All Wild Horses

"No one ever told me grief felt so like fear. The same fluttering in the stomach, the same restlessness, the yawning. I keep on swallowing. I find it hard to take in what anyone says. Yet I dread the moments when the house is empty."
C. S. Lewis

Grieving is oddly like jet lag. A couple of hours sleep so profoundly deep you assume it must be minutes before the alarm clock. Then a glance at the watch, and the luminous hands that blink cheerlessly back: 1:40 am. Then the fuzzy hours begin. The man reaches into his pocket to his papers. The moon is in wax, so he can make out the scrawl. The words spark up his blue world.

Some tributaries
are hidden from us

How to get
from here to there

We must keep our eyes wide
to the small ones;
the robin
with her lively messages
deep in the happy chapel
of her feathers.

The humiliation of being left. Being the one that stayed loving. How steadfastness of a sudden becomes a kind of shame, a defect, a lack. Naive. And that the world appraises us, actually admires us by our capacity to sever from an event of consequence, as if that constitutes *strength*. Emoji of triumphant woman, dusting herself down. You go girl.

To no longer stand in the glow of her love, to be outside it. To know that someone else does. And when they speak of them, a tear rolls down their face, just so you understand their depth of feeling. They want to communicate this, as if they are giving you a gift. And they squeeze your hand for understanding—*you are a good man*. Before you know it, you are carrying their bags down to the car. They have a little more make up on than usual, and there's the glimpse of an expensive bra strap.

Bell boy bell boy bell boy

And you get caught up with the sharp tang of change too, its liminal display that lifts such moments out of the mundane. Even in the agonies you are momentarily willing her on, wishing her well. Because we all want *something* just to know we're alive, and in the paucity of our times, we may just take heartbreak as our religious breakthrough. Maybe this is all for the good. Jump, sweetheart, jump. Run along. I'm still your rock.

And soon the new one stands alongside her under the warm light of Lantern Waste. He puts his expensive, protective arm round her and you are to shuffle off into the pine trees and the snow and the dark. Let the hawk pick at your wound. Die in private please. There's a good man. No need for the Shepherd's hook. You are simply not in her head anymore.

And the poets say something like: you look so together, the wreckage must be inside you.

And what if you don't want to be a good man anymore. He was wrong about her—she is a thoroughly modern woman after all. *She is modern, she is modern, she is modern.* No deeper insult.

You were a fool to love her.

You have become an object of her pity.

You are lesser in her eyes because of your love.

Not one of your books could have saved you.

✳✳✳

Dawn. It is the girl that sees it first. In fact hears it first. The sleek black cormorant sings its way steadily towards the raft. It shudders to a halt on the deck with unafraid eyes. Intelligent eyes. Versed in the old tales, the girl waits patiently for the cormorant to burst into the shape of a handsome young man with a harp or wizened crone or some such. It stays resolutely cormorant, but it can speak in a way she can comprehend.

"Like Tristan in his troubles you are, on the supple sea in your twigged craft. The wind murmurs you seek the south, to fling questions at the Olympians themselves. But I'm not convinced you have drunk deeply enough from your own island. Not at all."

Cormorant spits a streak of runny tobacco juice on the deck.

"Underneath these waters, the rough gods are commingling tonight, and that makes this not a place for your timbers. I'm staging an intervention, and getting you out." He will brook no debate.

And with that, the bird takes the front of the raft in an ever-growing beak and starts to pull it over the waves. Faster, a milky blur, a hallucinatory churning to the rocks and the coast and the bird's nest. To Wales. Not Greece, or anywhere near it.

Fuck, Wales. No disrespect *Myrddin Emrys, Dafydd Ap Gwilym, R.S. Thomas, dear boy-god Dylan.* We long for just a bit of sun, here on the planks. A little squid and ice-cold beer, a little tapas and funky old women in black shawls. The timber dwellers suspect the only part of that arrangement they will access is that very last detail.

Wales. How green is my bloody valley, how warm is my beer. Piping hot there love. Slurp down your scalding booze. Cardiff fists bare knuckling in the carparks, snowy eagles swooping from misty hill to misty hill, dropping pagan preachers from their claws into every chapel, five minutes before the toffee-chewing parishioners shuffle in, eyeing the bitter coffee and the scalding water heater. Chips and depression and ecstasy and lanes so slim they must have been interred by voles with a shovel. Poets so outstanding they seem branded by the Christ-light and confirmed by Geronimo, crammed up close to neurotic old England, England twisting its head away from the Red Dragon but forever triaded with those western Celts and the woaded eye-rollers of the North. Like a businessman squeezed up by frisky punk rockers on the tube. Wales, you great, beautiful mystery, another day please, we implore you.

On the coast the cormorant settles them in his thatchy home—of driftwood and washed up bottles, of bailing twine and doubloons, pebbled and louche-green with seaweed rope. Outside the rain sluices and the sea-a-rumbles. With their lanterns and bread and cheese, thick jumper apiece, they shelter as the bird rises with that characteristic half-unfolding of wing. In the flamboyant manner of Taliesin himself, their host announces:

Not the twelve-tyned stag am I
Or the salmon of the pool
Not favoured like the owl am I
Or the last wolf of Ceredigion

But cormorant I am
Black black black I am
And I will give you
A royal road into
The secret conscience of Cymru

I will give you
A binding, a branch
Of story for your raft
For your gathering up

With that, the bird clears his throat, slurps brown beer from a rock crevice and commits to revealing his bardic secrets.

"Enough with the vignettes, here's a main dish. You think love is simple man? It takes negotiation. It takes libation. It takes agitation. It's your own foolishness if you didn't know that. Here we go."

✳✳✳

Pwyll and Rhiannon

Pwyll, Prince of Dyfed had it in his mind to hunt.

And not just in his mind—but his heart, his whole constitution—to plunge deer tracks deep into the precinct of his kingdom they call Glyn Cuch. Compelled to push further, to loosen himself. Over the crunch of hazel nut and dying bracken he galloped, each green gully a station further from his everyday life. Each acre a doorway into the dreaming.

Supported by entourage, with hounds padding his hooves, when he blew his horn he became suddenly separated from his men. It was as if he banished them with the note. What arose was the Wyrd—the thrumming music of a chase, the crash of stag, the yap chatter of mutts elevated suddenly to a choir, but sung by beasts that were not his own. And it was those dogs that caught him, halted him, sobered him. It was their ghost shape. White as milk, almost glowing, ears scarlet, like jugs of blood.

But still he pushed on, making passage to claim the prize. Rallying his horse in circles to scatter the other dogs. Greed overrode uncanny knowing. As he squatted in the gutting river of blood, feeding his hounds, it was some dying part of himself he was also facing.

From the trees, a Grey Rider cantered toward him, austere, clearly a noble. A visitor from the Other Place.

"I know you but I will not greet you," he spoke. "That you would take another one's hunt. That you would drive away such hounds. Tsch. I will not take revenge, but know this: I will bring shame upon you to the value of a hundred stags."

To avoid such horror, Pwyll took a strange penance. The Grey Rider was Arawn, King of Annwfn, and he swiftly reported a way of culling the debt, though not without labour. You must know that Annwfn is the nearest Otherworld to ours.

Arawn leant forward on his saddle and laid out terms. "A chief's territory crashes against mine, crashes like storm waves on Anglesey. He's like a gull that breaks the necks of chicks. A bully. I can't endure it, but I can't quite win either. But you: I note your hero shape, how the woods bend towards you. With my magics I will give you my form, and no one, not even my wife or warriors, will know it is not I. For a year you will share her goodly bed, taste clear wine in cup, enjoy chops on your plate—and then you will go to the ford and meet him in single combat. His name? Hafgan.

You will defeat him with one deathblow. Just one. Resist the heat of a killer's arm. Because he will bound gladly up again, prick-stiff and laughing if you rain the blows down. They will revive him. I know this through sour experience.

I will go to your land and preside; I will take your posture. No one will know."

And from then on, the strange twinning began.

And it was just as Arawn said it would be.

Lodgings resplendent, fires that never went out, tapestry daubing the walls, golden vessels for roast venison and ruby splashed beer. Arawn's wife was magnificence; it was hard to look at her. But at night, when she lay warm and attentive in the dark next to Pwyll, he laid not one finger on her body. All year it would be the same. During the day he would be more than civil: engaging, robust, a wit—but at night he would turn his face to the wall and that would be that. And all around the court the forest would breathe with the Queen in her loneliness.

The day came for the
meeting at the grey ford

Pwyll no longer
in the jaunty silks of court

no longer heartened
by harp and keg

but leathered, trained, terrible
no weakness anywhere

as it must be
when you meet
at the grey ford

Each day in Arawn's shape had given one drop of luck and strength to Pwyll, so his road in the fight was of fire and swiftness, an absolutely unconquerable thing. His blow split the boss of Hafgan's shield, there was a wrench-grind-and-shatter of armour, and he flew the length of his nag and spear-shaft till he thumped vicious ground. From the tree line, Death the mid-wife tilted her head.

Hafgan bartered: "There is no way back to life for me after such a blow. No more spring bloom, no wine-maidens, no wintering tales. Please. Finish it."

Pwyll countered: "The surety of your death is for you to negotiate. I will not bless your lustre with a second blow, witch."

With that, Hafgan's nobles, encouraged by their lord, swore allegiance to Pwyll, and in doing so saved their lives. Hafgan's closest officers removed him from the ford for his dying time.

All shame lifted, Pwyll shook obligation from his shoulders and made his way back to Glyn Cuch—lighter, confirmed in some way. The Grey Rider was waiting.

In old, sing-song magic, the two men shifted shape, and shot back into their true frames, each blinking and laughing at their body's right feeling.

Arawn was happy to meet his warriors, to ruff the head of his hounds, to settle in his chair by the fire, but happiest of all was he to meet his wife. None, of course, any the wiser that they had not truly seen him for one year. He looked from the corner of his eye: there was no largeness of the Queen's belly, no sickness at the feast. And when later he reached for her in bed she came to him like a powerful, long-rumoured but rarely glimpsed river meets an ocean.

When the Grey Rider realized the quietness of his marital bed that last year, he confessed the strange arrangement. His wife was never more luminous to him than that night.

On Pwyll's return, he found he had never ruled so well by not actually being there: never so generous, even-handed, like a high kestrel in his far-ranging perceptions. The land, the animals, the people flourished. From that day, a rare thing leapt between the two chiefs: genuine friendship. They would send each other favoured hounds, horses, hawks, jewels. Goblets are still raised to their fellowship. Dyfed itself was twinned with Annwfn, that Otherworld, a braided knot. A spiritual pressure point in the ancient body of Britain.

When a leader displays such magnanimity, the world rushes to meet them. And soon Pwyll's reputation paced ahead of him. Too much for one to carry without a mate. One of his chief courts was at Arberth, and a feast was prepared for him there. The first sitting was so relentless in its sheer and wonderful glut, that the man took the air between servings. With a large retinue, he clambered the mound above the court, the place called Gorsedd Arberth. One of the men piped up, "A word, sire, about this tump. It is said, and truly I think, that whatever noble man sits on its grasses will experience one of two things: either a wound, or they will witness something wonderful".

Spoke Pwyll the Great Leader: "I have no fear of a wound surrounded by this beautiful flank of warriors, and I am always open to wonder." And so he and the men rested on the sweet grasses, patting their bellies and peering the hills. Not long to wait.

    Canter Canter Canter
She Comes Gliding
a woman
        such a woman to

tear and mulch the jaded heart.

We all long to fall
under such hooves

She rode a pale, milky horse, large and formal, and dressed in golden silk.

Not recognising her, and ablaze with possibility, a speedy rider was sent to try and talk. But no matter the strain and skill of the beast, it could never quite catch her. And always she seemed to glide, never breaking to a gallop. The rider returned to the tump and the teasing men. The next day was just like the first, till Pwyll himself elected to go. "This is clearly between god and me. Bring me my horse and my spurs."

Not long to wait, Pwyll provoked his horse to movement, but even he, with his skill and his horse's nimble leaps, could not compete. He rasped a request at last:

"Maiden, in the name of the man you love the most, please wait for me."

She immediately halted. "Of course, happily. You may have made things easier for your horse if you'd asked some time back!" She waited for the exhausted chief, and drew back her headdress and fixed true gaze on him. Strong gaze.

"Lady. Lady—where have you come from, where are you going?"

"Well, going my business. And I am happy to see you."

"My welcome to you," spoke up Pwyll, and never more had he meant it. Pwyll of the scars, Pwyll of the hunt, Pwyll of the shape-leap, Pwyll of the grey ford, big Pwyll was quite undone. Giddy. "What's the business, may I ask?"

"My main purpose was for us to meet."

"That's the best business I ever heard of," spoke Pwyll. "Would you tell me your name?"

"Rhiannon. I am Rhiannon, daughter of Hyfaidd Hen.
Given to be wedded to a man against my will. Because
of my love for you, I do not want him. So I come to
find out your answer on the matter."

Pwyll gathered himself.

"These words can be tested by god:
if all women and maidens were made
available to me, it is
you that I would choose."

Earth bows at such straight talkers.

"Good. *Good.* Well, before I am given to another,
arrange a meeting with me.
Claim me. As I am claiming you.
A year from tonight there will be a feast
prepared in the court of my father.

Lord, do not forget your promise."

And with that, she turned and left. But her warmth remained. For that moment on, Pwyll would not be drawn on the subject of the Queen of the Horses, not even to his closest. Some things are just too sweet to share.

The year was up, a year of imaginings, a secretive croft attended by the milky dreams of the chief. He arrived, resplendent, at the court of Hyfaidd, with no less than ninety men in his retinue. Rhiannon's very greeting to him caused kindling to spark, the table to groan with feast, the bard to reach new heights of eloquence. Something immense was about to occur. The arrangement of the hall was this: Hyfaidd Hen at the centre, Pwyll on one side, Rhiannon on the other, and then each according to rank and honour. A just hierarchy, from a time when such things existed, and will again.

Some time into the feast, a young lad entered the hall. Despite his youth he had weight, fledgling presence even. Tall, auburn haired, silk across his shoulders, a pout. He sauntered his way to the high end of the hall, and addressed Pwyll. "Lord. My business here is with you. I have a favour to ask."

Generosity, the key to a real leader.
And a key to their derailment.

The words come almost in slow motion, before the Horse Maiden could cram them back in her suitor's mouth. "Whatever you request, as long as I have it, it is yours."

Rhiannon gasps, and a mare gallops a lonely valley. "Why, why did you respond so?"

"Well, he has," pipes the lad, "and the gentry have heard it. My request, oh big-hearted Pwyll, is for the woman you wish to marry, and her provisions too." Wide smirk, the hint of a bow.

Pwyll sunk into horror. As deep as Cheddar Gorge, as bleak as winter on Caer Idris. He was without speech. Rhiannon, not so.

"This is the boy they wished me to marry. Gwawl, son of Clud, a powerful man, of heft and ambition, drunk with followers. Godlike. And now you must give me to his son, or risk disgrace."

Not for the first time, we remember.

Pwyll stirred from his bleak shore. "I can't do this. I can't. I can't."

She drew him close. "He asks for my provision: this feast. That is not in your power to provide. I will give it to him, every chop, pudding, fruit and wine. He and his entourage will be sick with luxury. Little heroes, they will think themselves. Titans. Pats on the back. I will then arrange a meeting, in a year's time, to sleep with him. At that time you will hide out in the orchard with ninety-nine men, and I will give you a bag to bring. In the feasting, as he gazes over at the acres he thinks he is soon to plough, stagger in as a beggar. Call him on his own game. Generosity. And ask for nothing but this little bag to be filled with food. Such a small act. But if all the meat of Dyfed were to be placed in it, it would not be filled.

He will be sure to enquire on its appetite, and tell him that only an extremely powerful, nay, virile, nobleman could tread the food down in the bag, so would it cease its chomping. I will see to it that he parades such vanity as to clamber in. When he comes, turn the bag over so he is head over heels, tie up the neck, call your men of the orchard with your horn, and let them descend, descend with their fierce faces."

Gwawl called the high table again, flushed now with his success. "I need a reply."

"As much as it is in my power to supply, so you shall have." A roar from the gleeful warriors. Outfoxed the big man.

But not Rhiannon.

A year later the meeting took place. The secret troupe stood steady under the apple bough, and Pwyll made good show as a beggar. Stinking, bloodied rags, a mess. A request for a bag of food, nothing less. Ah, but the bag was hungry. Starving even. A hundred years without so much as crumb.

Gwawl bellowed: "What is wrong with the bag? Our provisions are being gulped!"

Pwyll crooned, respectfully, "It requires a firm and noble man to step into the bag, push the food down further and say, 'Enough has been put in here'." At this, for a second, Rhiannon gently touched the arm of the boy. "My man. My bull. Get up quickly."

A rush of blood. He leapt, blissful into the bag. Bag was tipped, tied, and horn blown. From the place of the apples the men came. As each entered, each man struck a firm blow to the bag. Ninety-nine resolute, breathless blows.

"What's in the bag?"

"A badger. A badger in the bag."

At this, a voice croaked up from the swill. "Lord, this game of badger in the bag will soon kill me. I beg you. Slaughtering me like this is not how I should die."

And this was how the pup saved his own life. He scampered from the hall and if you put your ear to the ground you will hear him scampering still.

From then on, they were grand to their people, Rhiannon and Pwyll. At the court in Arberth they presided over a huge range of guests, none of whom left without ring, brooch or wealthy stone. All felt confirmed, raised up in their presence, witnessed. That was the true gift.

But after three years, visitors started to steal little glances at the Queen's belly. Still trim, no jut of a male heir. A dangerous situation. A group of noblemen had enough political heft to summon Pwyll, to Preseli in Dyfed. And there did they press him to take another wife, for the sake of the kingdom. They were clear that the honeymoon was over.

But Pwyll fought for his love, and gained another year till the council would meet again and only then would he accede to the wider good. And in that year Rhiannon did indeed begin a lovely turn of shape. Goodness, magic, and the deep mother were what her baby suckled on, there in the warm byre of her womb.

But strange   strange   strange

On the night of the birth—a boy
six women stayed up
watching over the mother and child

Six women fell asleep
before the cock crowed

Six women greasy with fear
when they saw that the baby
had been
spirited away.

They knew it was their own deaths they were facing. And not swift. Some awful thought shook the women—like a possession—and they daubed sleeping Rhiannon's face with the blood of pups, and when she woke, they screamed and moaned that she had destroyed her own son, wrestling him from them.

Many times Rhiannon offered them pardon for truth telling, but so queasy were they that they gripped to the shrillness of their fiction. Rat a tat tat. For the rest of their days they would have an ear for the battering on the door, the arrival of the king's men. Their sleep would be thin.

Stories like that have traction, are hard to conceal. The nobles brought the full weight of the law down on the back of heartbroken Pwyll, but still he refused to divorce. But what was the truth of it all?

His grief made him blurry. He lost discernment in his wretched anxiety. Lost connection with the Otherworld. With his wife. With himself. After counsel with learned people, Rhiannon decided to accept punishment, than the drawn out scrap with six treacherous women.

The punishment? To sit by the mounting block outside the gate to Arberth, and tell her story to anyone she thought may not know it. And to carry guests to court if they so desired it. Few did. But there she sat, through sleet and thin snow, holding in her mouth a story that never was. Seven years was the decree. At the end of the day she would trudge back to court. At night she would stand by her window.

While Rhiannon of the horses stood,
her arms outstretched in the dark,

equine energies worked
tirelessly for her.

✳✳✳

In Gwent
Teyrnon Twrf Liant
was lord, and in
his house lived
a mystery.

He had a mare that every May Eve would give birth, an elegant animal, unrivalled. But the foal would always immediately disappear. Finally, roused through conversation with his wife, he brought the horse indoors and armed himself as the foal was born. There it shuddered, a spring wonder, a budding leaf, a green wave in the bay. Even as he walked over to test its weight, a vast claw shot through the window and grabbed the babe by its mane. Teyrnon was ready and gave one cutting blow down on the arm. Part of the arm, and the foal slid down the wall of his house, the tiny horse safe. Outside, the darkness was shudder-shake with the scream of the beast and the lord staggered through the door to finish it, but could not make out a form in the black.

When he returned to the doorway
he found a bundle,
a Moses, a Taliesin,
there in the candlelight

A swaddling of brocaded silk
a summering field of golden curls
strong arms, chubby and waving,
a cub reaching hard for life's pap

Though they could not help but love this spring arrival, as word passed from travellers of Rhiannon's situation, suspicion grew in the couple as to the boy's parentage. And he carried his mother's loves: by four years old he was negotiating with stable boys to water the horses. He couldn't stay away from them. In the end, they gave the lad the very horse that had been born the night he had been found. He and his wife turned it endlessly round in their conversations. Teyrnon's wife finally concluded:

"If we send the boy home we will receive three things: the gratitude of Rhiannon for being released from her fiction and punishment; thanks from Pwyll for raising the boy; and finally, if he has conscience he will be our foster son and provide for us."

They agreed to take him to them, blew the candle on the decision, went to bed.

When they arrived at the gate of Arberth, Rhiannon offered to carry them to the court. Such was her strength she could have done it. But of course, no one wished it. Soon the tables were being gold plated with food and drink, the embers stirred and great logs lain on their coals. Rhiannon was back from her daily sojourn at the gate, and Pwyll just returned from a circuit of Dyfed. When they saw the three visitors, they batted other business aside to get to the travellers' story.

There was no shred, no follicle, no thin strand of doubt that this was their son. It was truth. Like sea spray and sunlight and foxgloves. Truth that breaks the fear-spell. Teyrnon raised himself and gave good story of the whole affair—the magic of May Eve, the foal, the black arm, the babe wrapped in silk.

And each word of the story worked on the skin and the flesh and the bone of Rhiannon, and scoured all possible confusion from Pwyll's heart. They would weave those broken years back together. Sing the old grief song onto poetry's hazels. It would be a kingdom renewed.

Rhiannon gave the name of Pryderi to their son. Her boy of the horse-blood and the May Eve.

Pryderi
who ruled the seven districts
of Dyfed, who conquered the
three cantrefs of Ystrad Tywi,
and the four cantrefs of Ceredigion—
the seven cantrefs of Seisyllwch.

***

The cormorant demands a round of applause and gets one. This story is harder to grasp than some of the others. More mythological, less personal. But the bird insists that's what love is. It's not to be taken personally. It's big ugly forces burning through you. In a time of insurance policies it's a unique opportunity to still get fried alive by the gods.

In the nest, the girl is drawing Rhiannon, over and over. A horsy woman. A woman that is a horse. She bends her head but keeps drawing and asks:
"Is Mum secretly an animal? Have all your girlfriends been animals really? Or fairies? Or star formations?"

He laughs. That would explain alot. Maybe distant planets circling Saturn. They make a list. Or as many as the man is ready to talk about.

The girl thinks about betrayal for a long time. Of having the blood of pups smeared on your sleeping face. It's hard being a girl.

If your lover is an animal or a star or a spirit, to what must be they loyal? Do you serve in the same temple? Or are you just a badger in their bag?

A badger in their bag baby, that's all you ever were to her.

"I have a story for that," says the cormorant, reading his thoughts.

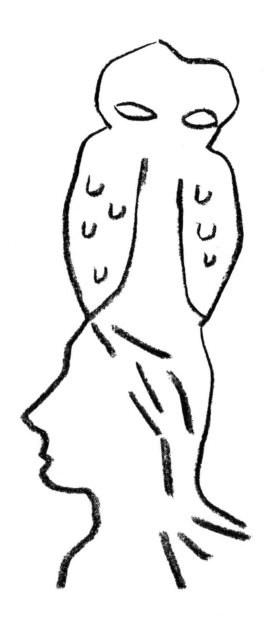

Chapter Seven

Woman is a Wild Thing

"A man should not love the moon."
Czeslaw Milosz

Early morning in the nest, and the girl is making a list of her favourite stories so far. Definitely tops is Tatterhood, with Vasya Whitefoot a fairly distant second. She's still thinking about the Fox Woman story, and wonders what it means to not be able to go home anymore. She feels bad for the fox.

The story the cormorant told is a little unwieldy, like it's being told in a language she can only half understand. It's more like a puzzle, something to be turned around in her mind again and again, from many angles. A mythic Rubik's Cube. She thinks this is hilarious.

Dad liked it though, she notes. He perked up when Rhiannon appeared. His cheek flushed, though he acted casual. She looks at him sleeping, his head on his bundled up leather jacket. For a long time she has known he has been sad. She worries about it but she doesn't tell him. Every time someone in a movie with a beard dies, she cries.

She has brought a little gas canister in from the raft for coffee for her and him. She's only just started drinking it—and not at his strength—but she loves to hold his mug in both hands and blow steam from it, like she's having a great idea.

Soon cormorant is about, in all his wizarding stature, and he pecks again at the pool of brown beer and begins his second story. He pecks on his fragment of washed up blackboard to signify class is in session. Up in his nest, as the rest of the world goes to hell in a handbag, the two of them sit with rapt focus, as if it's the most natural and needed thing in the world, this myth-telling of a cormorant.

Speak, oh bird of stature and language,
Badass magus of the bleak shore,
Tell us of all that passed and matters,
And speak to our times too

✳✳✳

Blodeuedd of the Flowers

They all knew Llew was handsome. Llew Llaw Gyffes: laughing boy, stag proud, wheat-blond, a lively wit but gracious to all—a catch. Surely one parade of the market square, one giddy night of dancing would secure him a wife?

No.

Years before, his own mother had bent her calm finger in his direction and swore that he would never take a wife from any race on this earth. Oh, he could rut till he was giddy, grow hair-backed and barking in the May Day rituals, but no deeper union would be his. He would never truly be rooted to a woman. With her hex she thinned his lovemaking, cut the banks of wild flowers to a buzz trim, drained his forest pool of all its gloaming fishes.

Bait would drag his shallows and no more.

Off you go, lover man.

Llew's uncle, Gwydion, was a witch of repute, and he observed this crippling with a keen eye. He saw his sweet nephew grow thinner with each amorous clamber, a waning not suited to his years. Vast Gwydion resolved to help. With another cunning man, Math, they looked hard to find cracks in the old bitch's casting.

"On this earth?" they asked each other. "What if she was not from this earth?"

With their night intelligence they packed provisions for a quest—a hunter's kit—and made for the black hills. Shuddering in gale, salmon-pinked by sun they scooped up flowers of the oak, the golden broom, and the far-laced meadow sweet. Tumps of wild blossoms, heaped like a woman's curves, until a body was arrayed on the sweet grasses. A fume-tangle of heavy scent, of delicate buds and foliaged beauty.

Then they muttered with their stubbled jaws, cast great arcs of potion liberally over the sex, the heart, the brain of this leafy thing. This great ship of flora, wet-rooted in the underswing of earth, drawn up into collaboration with freezing blue stars.

Proper magic.

Wild geese in the smoky air, peered down into the changeling, a shape alive—shifting in invisible gusts, rootsy hips, mooned face, scalding the wetling grasses.

It was two who went up.
It was three that came down from the hills.

They named her Blodeuedd—"Flowers". Her eerie beauty caught Llew agape, one glance at her threshold and he threw all of his affections into the pen of love's wild horses. Soon, they married—Blodeuedd and Llew—that elemental woman and the lad of the valleys.

One morning, some time later, whilst Llew was abroad with Math, Blodeuedd was roused by a horn outside the castle. From her window she saw in the morning fog, a stag burst from the thicket; and then foam-jawed hounds and behind them huntsmen—a formal line of pursuit, ancient and stylish. Their beholding was like a bell ringing inside her; like a scene from a tapestry.

Their leader? Gronw, lord of Penllyn. The flower maiden catches just a second of his dark shape cantering by, but it is enough. Maybe some copsy scent clung to the Hunter-Lord, maybe he smelt of her home, of earth. He was a deep music to her green inner form.

That evening the men are invited to supper and to lodge in the castle.

Thatched torches are lit in the stone corridors, mead sweetens the salt from the chops, the gallery swells with minstrels. In the candled gloom, love and its transgressions rise up between Blodeuedd and Gronw.

It is one thing to feel, quite another to act. Still, they do. Her boy-husband might be riding his horse off the very edge of the world for all she knew, or cared. In the nights they spent together, their trysting grew bolder, requiring broader ground.

"How do we rid ourselves of Llew?" mutters the suitor, sourly.

"He is riddled with enchantments," she says. "There must be a science to his dying—that I shall make my business to gather."

Gronw nods, unblinking.

When Llew returns, his wife is remote—swathed in distance—all to herself. The merry stories of his journey fall sour between them. Groping into the air, panicked, he asks about her silence—Was she sick? She gathered her fiction: "Not sick, beloved, but worried. Anxious that one day you may die and I would have to live on."

Relieved at her concern, he speaks with confidence, "Ah, well if that is all, I have good news. The killing of me would not be an easy thing. The murderer would need information only the gods could supply."

Blodeuedd leaned in now, flushed. "Ah such good news! Please, put my mind at rest, tell me something of its nature, so I can put such crow-aches from my heart."

He reveals: "Certainly. I can only be butchered by the tip of a spear that has taken a year to create, and the forging of such a spear can only be on the morning hours of a Sunday, when all are worshipping.

I cannot be killed in a house or outside a house. Not on horseback or on foot. The only way it could happen is like this: a bath would be made upon a river bank, and roofed with thatch. A goat would be produced and tethered by the tub.

If I placed one foot on the goat, and one on the rim of the bath, and if that spear was thrown, then, and only then, could I be slain."

His wife absorbed the facts, nestled them in her breast, steadied the information, and got message to Gronw. With his fierce face and skilled hand he slipped to the forge in the praying times of every Sunday and got to work. Outside of chapel's godly care, he plied his terrible attentions, blistered his paws, was grunt-back-bent over the hot iron.

It took one year, but Gronw made the spear. The Flowered Wife did not forget him, did not veer from the plan.

Blodeuedd spoke up to Llew. "Sweetheart. Indulge me. I still am fearful of your death. Would you not consider creating the very scene that you described—the bath, the goat? So that I can see just how unlikely it would be that such forces would align.

In the seeing of it somehow I believe my fear would set me free."

Lacking the foresight of an older man, Llew agreed to the request, eagerly producing the materials for his own ambush. Blodeuedd sent word to Gronw the dark.

She prepared the bath on the river bank, made sure the water was warm, and scented with sweet herbs. Llew sloshed about, then settled in his wife's attention. She produced a rugged brown goat. "Now darling—could you just rise and show me how you would balance on the goat and the tub?"

Naked, the trusting husband rose, dripping and shivering in cold Welsh air, gingerly balancing on the edge of the tub, placing his right foot upon the goat's curved back. When his wobbling settled, when he was clearly in place, Blodeuedd let out the death-shriek she had held so long, and from the bleak copse emerged Gronw. With the strength of his father, and his father's father, he hurled the spear straight at the trembling form of Llew.

Such was the force that when it hit Llew—in the side of his body—the shaft broke off and the head of the spear stayed embedded in the wound. Screaming, stricken, rough with blood, Llew spasmed into eagle-shape, a man no more and, with head of the spear still gutted-fast, flew from sight.

Time passes. Cold news of the betrayal reaches Gwydion and Math, the Frankensteins to this floral deceiver.

Low with worry, Gwydion stalks the land: the seaports, the humped and rutted tracks of farmers, looking for a hint of where the bird-wound-man has gone. Around his raw knuckles he wraps prayer-words that this boy still lives. Many would have given up.

One day in early winter, he comes to a farm. Frost has stiffened his cloak, aches abide in his bone-house. Talking to the swineherd about anything unusual in the local weather, movement of animals, the magics of the settlement.

The farm boy has one thought only: of a sow that trots briskly when the sty is opened across the frozen soil and out into the forest, never followed by others; always returning drowsy and content. A thin lead, indeed, but perhaps enough.

Enough for Gwydion to take a night's rest at the place. At dawn he strolls in cold gold light along the sow's trail. Upstream, he follows, then across scattered fields, further over hills to a quiet valley. The sow waddles to a fat-trunked oak, its northern flank moss-thick. In the muddied roots the beast starts to snuffle and over the minutes that follow, a shower of ripe flesh begins to fall from the higher branches, to the grunting pleasure of the sow.

Glancing up, at the very top of the tree, the uncle spies an eagle, loosening a treasure of maggoted meat to its slobbering ally at the base. Gwydion knew the inner-shape of that bird. So he began to sing—

"Between two lakes an old oak grows,
sheltered from cold wind that blows

I know I do not tell a lie—
My nephew Llew rests there on high."

Cocking his head, the eagle
dropped from the high branches to the middle.

"There is an oak on an upland plain,
not scorched by sun, or wet with rain;
may his hardships soon be o'er
And Llew restored to us once more."

Again the eagle dropped down now
to the lowest branches.

For the final time, Gwydion sang—

"Grows an oak upon a steep
Where a lord his home does keep,
If I do not speak falsely,
Llew will come on to my knee"

The eagle alighted onto Gwydion's knee.

With a small cut of rowan branch, the enchanter stroked the back of the eagle's head, shape-lurching back into Llew, scrappily awake, deep flustered, naked and blue-skinned on the winter turf. Just an imprint of his former self. Crumpled, and shrunk, not quite alive.

Wrapping him in his cloak, Gwydion shouldered as best he could the shrunken man, his bird-voice adrift between species. At the chambers of Math, the greatest of physicians attended from all sides. He raged, sweat-shimmered through blue night, slammed his forelock on the buttress of death; floundered through shape again and again. Sometimes tufted, sometimes a bone-cairn. Only gradually, like the wheeling seasons, buds of green appeared through the ice-sheets of his illness.

✳✳✳

They all knew Llew was handsome. But now they'd find that he was deadly.

Gronw, when he heard of this return, shat hot liquid, a-quake with fear for what was coming.

He sends over parley of silver, and gold, but he finds deaf ears. Llew demands meeting by the very spot where the spear was thrown. Black Gronw became Gronw of the Grovel, as he begs for a stone to be placed between the two men, for he knows the man means to hurl his spear. When Llew agreed, Gronw produced nothing less than a granite block higher than a man to stand between them.

No matter.

It was an ancient spear, and whetted with cave magic it split the rock like summer butter, and skewered the lord fast to the dark pitch of soil. For Gronw, no swift ending.

It was Gwydion who tracked his creature down, the Woman of the Flowers. In a place far from villages, surrounded by maidens, who wailed through the drizzle mist when the death-magus slowly cantered towards them, his long fingers hexing their mistress.

As one, they moved backwards, paying no mind to the ancient lake abiding behind them. The hooves of their steeds sliding mad on the guttered banks, as the green-lipped eye of the dreaming waters rose and took them down under the singing roof of wave.

Only Blodeuedd was still, her horse jaded by the magnetism of the wizard.

"Slaying," spoke Gwydion, "is not my business with you. But some other hurt I will provoke. Oh I release you from this human form, Blodeuedd. You will be a bird. But a bird that will not feel sun caught in its feathers. Ebony wanderer, moon-faced, trouble-hunted by all other birds, an owl you will be.

This is your difficult trail, faithless one."

But what had she been faithless to?
                    Did anyone ask of the gods she followed?

This harm falls at her creator's hand too, surely.

These thoughts ride alongside.

On the back of her head, he tapped once with his wand and her face, for a second, was a-blaze again with flowers. Her eyes rolled back in their foliaged pits, with an eerie goodness, a body lit from inside. Then taking the luna-round shape of the gloaming bird.

The owl thrust out,
        took wing and was gone
gone beyond,
        deep into the wet flank of the woods

✳✳✳

There's a long silence after the story. The cormorant, rather theatrically, has placed a little seaweed cloak round his shoulders to recover from the rigour of the telling. A beaky James Brown, a Muhammad Ali of the feathered world.

"That is *not* a love story," says the girl. "I liked it, it was really odd, but it's *not* a love story. It's not fair."

The man tends to agree. "It's a set up. The woman was made from flowers, why can't she just be with who she wants? Though I loved to hear of the spearing. Yes. There should be such an allowance for lovers who have been stuck up a tree as a butchered eagle all winter. And anyway, what's so bad about being turned into an owl?"

The cormorant sighs, "Your ears are not tuned, not tuned, not tuned anymore to the real implications of the story. Always with the auditions. Stop telling the story what it is."

The girl is thinking, thinking hard. She remembers something a friend of her Dad's had talked about, a gifted anthropologist, that in a tribe in the Amazon where she'd lived, it's understood that woman's original marriage was to the wild, not to a man. That a man actually had to stand in the way of that relationship for anything much to happen between them. It was almost a kind of kidnapping they had to do.

Maybe some women are made of flowers. Maybe some women are wild. Maybe some women are owls. No wonder things go crazy in little houses on the edge of town. Some big part of them, some original part of them, is wedded to something else entirely.

✳✳✳

As the morning continues and the weight of the two stories of instruction lands somewhere deep and tangly in their bellies they prepare to leave the care of the cormorant. But in the final minutes of their time, something extraordinary happens. Something the man has known about but never thought he'd see. Bardic combat.

Of a sudden, a hawk swirls into the compound, the nest of the cormorant. The cormorant unfurls himself quickly, they circle and start to compose in nimble combat. It's that quick, the happening.

Hawk: *A question, O bird of dark speech, from where have you come?*

Cormorant: *Not hard to answer. From the heel of a sage, a gathering of wisdom, goodness's perfection, from the bright sunrise, from the hazels of poetic skill—where righteousness is learnt and falsehood falls, where colours are witnessed and poems are made vivid and fresh. And you, my senior, where do you come from?*

Hawk: *Not hard to answer. I have flown over the columns of the ages and the streams of Leinster, over the Elfmound of Nectan's wife, the forearm of Nuada's wife, from the land of the sun and the dwelling of the moon, from the navel-string of youth. A question, oh lad of language, what is your name?*

Cormorant: *I am anger of fire and fire of speech, noise of knowledge and wellspring of wealth, sword of song. And you, my elder, what is your name?*

Hawk: *Not hard to answer. Most accurate in divination, champion of interrogation, enquirer of science and weft of art, a casket of poetry and all the abundance of the sea. A question, oh young instructor, what art do you practice?*

Cormorant: *I foster poetry and diffuse knowledge, I search for fame and woo science, my speech is the cattle of a sage, I bring tales as slick as my black feathers, that delight all sophisticated kings. And you, my professor, what do you practice?*

Hawk: *I establish peace and celebrate art, I hunt for support of kings, I enflame the fury of inspiration but promote tidy structure of mind, the art of a small poem with clear arrangement and a celebrated road. A question, young evangelical, what is your quest?*

Cormorant: *To walk the plains of age after the mountains of youth, to walk between candle and fire, battle and horror, to dwell most deeply within the streams of knowledge. And you, ancient one, what is yours?*

Hawk: *To have knowledge and carry in my breast the skill of poetic revision, to come to my death with abundance of honours. And you, spring morning, on what path have you come?*

Cormorant: *Not hard to answer. The white track of knowledge, through the curls of a king's beard, on the back of a ploughing-ox, on the dew of a goddess—both corn and milk. And you, dusk of magnificence, on what path have you come?*

Hawk: *On the breasts of soft women and the head of a spear, on a gown of silver, on a chariot with no need of wheels, on the three ignorances of the Mac ind Oc. And a question, youthful river, for whose son are you?*

Cormorant: *Not hard to answer. I am the Lad of Poetry, Poetry son of Close Attention, Close Attention son of Meditation, Meditation son of Lore, Lore son of Enquiry, Enquiry son of Investigation, Investigation son of Great Knowledge which is the son of Understanding which is the son of Wisdom, Wisdom being son of the three Gods of Poetry. And you, Full Moon Standing, whose son are you?*

Hawk: *Not hard to answer. I am son of the man who has been and was not born, buried in his mother's womb, baptised after death.*

At this, and for no reason the watchers can quite figure, the dialogue halts.

Cormorant: *I know you are wisest of prophets, you carry poetry's hazels in your beak, I know that god has brought you here, and I bow before you.*

And the cormorant does just that, and half un-curls his wings in true deference.

Chapter Eight

The Sherwood Croft

You should know, hawk really did make quite the entrance. That processional of words, the sheer plumage of his dexterity. It's not clear why the skirmish took place, it was rather like a zen priest suddenly barging into his student's digs and flattening him with koans. But for his part, it's clear that cormorant, though the junior partner, held up his end well. The surprise interrogation is over.

Hawk has a long way to fly. Not out over the waves but inland to a forest in England's heart, *the* forest in England's heart: where *Much the Miller's son, Little John and trusty Will Scarlet* wait for him by a fire that never goes out. At this news, dad and daughter lean forward, agog at the disclosure. They would be hard pressed to name much they love more than Robin Hood. They relay their admiration and the hawk takes it in as his due, as a custodian of dear Sherwood.

England. Hawk will fly—proper bird with a heart banging in its feathered chest— over the snake of her motorways and housing estates, over the crammed-in fields of the midlands, till he finally swoops down into that most secretive forest of Sherwood, into the conscience of the sovereignty of the land itself. Ted Hughes spied him over dawn fields and committed him to ink, pushed the hugeness of his own form into hawk's wingspan. It was that same hawk. Keep looking up.

But as hawk prepares to leave he stops, and leans in confidentially, (knowing he is in a Learning House) and drops a coin in the well of the collective knowledge:

"I will leave you with a secret, it is not Marion that waits with Robin in the Greenwood, but someone far older, whose name is deserving of the telling. I give you these words, still found on your ballad singers' lips from time to time. Let me tell you of Robin's true wife."

✳✳✳

Clorinda, Queen of the Shepherds

Robin of our dreaming,
Robin of the bough,

laughing boy, firm in the scrum,
our best.

The greening conscience of Merlin's Enclosure. He roars ablaze in you as you
protect what you honestly, truly love, as you un-shackle your guile from the
slithered seductions of the state, are nimble in the face of a brute, find paradise
in a poacher's fire, choice companions and a hundred thousand stars. He is loved,
utterly, this Pan of the North Country.

But who does *he* love?

Robin places his light foot on the grasses of Sherwood. He winds his horn—that
clear call through shrub and oak—dappling the ripples of the grey pool, challenging
you to live, to dare, to kiss the wounded. It is a sound that breaks morbid centuries,
tablets of stone, grubby spells, ruptures the fetid will of all tyrants. It makes you
cry to hear it. It hurts. It was what you loved before the world bent you. His
stag-sounding brings twenty-five men to his side. And they flushed to be in his
company. Counting themselves adrift in luck. Golden. The true Rebel-King of
Inner Britain. Arthur's secret twin.

But twenty-five is not enough for our man.
He needs more than forty. His calm eyes scout.
He spots others, sheltered and aghast under the green wood tree.
They do not catch his eye.

Today another charisma has risen—an equal—charm-rattled and rain-danced
from the very mulch and mist of the archaic woodland. She. She has their gaze
completely.

Clorinda. Queen of Shepherds.
Buskin to her knee, gown of velvet,
bow in her hand, clear as a warrior,
full quiver of arrows dangling her side.

No jut of pride, just steady,
steady like the rowan when it reddens.
Steady like the blue perched owl.
The forest is in her as well as around her.

Dark flow is her locks
Snow drifting skin.

I come to kill a fat buck,
for tomorrow is Titbury day.

The two are immediately in step. The animal powers leap towards such a fusion: two hundred bucks break from the green and Clorinda loosens the arrow that cannot swerve—the largest beast is thrust clean and through. Its furry, dying dreams nuzzle her white hand.

A match, a mate, it's never too late.

There is feasting as there must be. Honeycomb, dark mead, pie and venison roasting. Clorinda asks for the name of the twinkling man. In the ever-dusk, little wisps of light move near him.

Robin Robin Robin
Just like the Stories.
Just like the Rumours.

Clorinda, my step is noble
but I will roam always in
merry Sherwood.
It is my delight.

Be my wood-bride
Be my miracle.

Sometimes it is that simple. The swiftness of his love is a mirror of her arrow's surety. She finds it all delicious. And the old fairy colours mark her: the flush red of a love-cheek, the ivory neck, the coal-dark of her mane. Her delight is the very same as his. The feasting forest, the quiet pool, the nesting den of the moon-blessed lovers.

Be my wood-husband.

The air is suddenly hurled a-clatter with male singing; warm and gleeful, each note now a star that hangs above our head. But Clorinda must honour that Titbury feast, and issues invitation to her love: the first glimpsing of Robin in the wider world for an age. *Will your thigh brush mine under the feasting table?* Ah, Clorinda of the many wonderful persuasions. Clorinda of the copse, not the court. Calling Robin further into life.

Robin's Yeoman takes down another six brace of bucks, a treasury of flesh. But when you carry goods like that you call the thief to your table. Just five Staffordshire miles has eight men, boozed with bravery and flailing blades for the meat. Robin and John gather themselves, show the poetry of their violence and soon only three remain, scampering piss-wet to their wives. A sturdy reputation doesn't grow out of nowhere. It has to be earned.

This battle is fought near Titbury town, in the festival of the bull running, when bagpipes inflame their bovine mind. This skirmish is witnessed by the King of the Fiddlers, and he rarely swears his truth—but today he does. Here with us.

Clorinda sang:

Hey derry-down!
The bumpkins are beaten, put up your sword, Bob,
and now let's dance into the town.

Bull-energy has claimed the square. Blossom garlanded on shining horns, youths afire the sturdy back: some beat the blackthorn cudgel of the Morris, others caw the ballad *"Arthur-a-Bradley"*. All are a shudder, a quake with the possibility of true marriage. The town still receives its loamy messages of the bough.

Roger the Parson comes, fast from the district of Dubbridge, with holy and happy words, mass book and a clasping of hands. A steamy curled circle of beasts and royal peasants surrounds the marriage. Southern gods stomp grapes for the wine of the people, to make good and hot the sap between King and Queen. Children gaze on, wolfhounds nap. And the hawk by the well sees it all.

These two,
so deep in Britain's dreaming,
are walking back into the forest that always is.

They are walking back into you.
Meet them on the Royal Road.

For one hour, more or less, so great is the joy that every bird sings its green croon into the air. Garlanded by the woodsman, praised as Queen of the Forest, not just Shepherds, she and her groom dance through the blue smoke, leap the fire, straight and wonderful onto the fragrant rushes of their wedded bed.

Of what they did there
must stay private with me,
because they lay long the next day;
and I had to go home, but got a good piece
of bride-cake, and so came away.

In the forest that always is,
there is always the lover's croft,
the laughing folk of the bough,
and the slow shifting flanks of bucks in the dusk.

✳✳✳

"Never give up on love," says Hawk.

"Oh fuck," says Dad.

Chapter Nine

There is a Man Who Never Dries Out

And with that, the two raggeds left the byre of the cormorant and bellowed to the winds:

Hey Arcadia!
Even you great Artemis!
We're coming, but our raft
Is playing truant on Celtic currents!

Then they slept, on blue sea and under blue night they slept.

The man wakes to the sound of gulls.

They come to a prison.

Up ahead. It's a stony tower, circled by bronze on its base, on a steep outcrop of rocks. Glancing round they can see the waters have pushed them north again overnight.

They have come to Lost Boys' Rock.

The beautifully bleak rim of England's northwest coast is just within view.

He waves over at The Beatles, The Stone Roses, The La's, waves at the Viking mysteries of the Wirral, waves at Gawain on Gringolet his faithful steed searching for the Green chapel. All that music floating out into the Irish Sea. Intoxicating as it may be, it's still the wrong bloody direction. Greece this is not. Love aims for Athens and arrives at Bolton-on-Sea. Pray for a harsh instructor say the Sufis.

The kid is wrapped up in Dad's leather jacket. He remembers carrying her around in it when she was just a few months old, feeling like he had all the gold in the world in him. His charge, that was the word, his *charge*. Every old one in the family coughed quietly and muttered, "Don't fuck it up son." Sleep on, love.

What island is this, dear Athena? He knows what the tower is; it's for the lost boys, the toughs, the shell suited and booted, the scum on the shoe of the class under the working class. Inventive, quick-witted and fur-flicked coyotes, storming the palace every day of their brief and churning lives. Over the years he's been around and woven through the lives of hundreds of them.

And this place here, this place is every squashed-up, cash-strapped detention centre he's ever visited, just seen through a real lens for a moment, not that mucky shard of Coke glass we sometimes call 'real life'. Good god. *"Keep it un-real"* is what the rappers should preach. Enough already.

There is a bin bag stashed up to the side of the one huge door. That's where the innocence of the boys gets dumped. Innocence is a sweet-smelling grey-green stone. A whiff of it on the inside and you are dead meat. You are innocent if you commit the same crime over and over again and expect a different result. At some point, for the boys of the dark, this has to stop. You can be the wiliest thief for a hundred villages, and still some part of you is a kid running through the corn. The 'white shadow' the shrinks call it. But not in there, you are carrion now boy, a carrion artist.

This is not a place he wants his daughter to see. He stands up, tottering a little, and, for the first time, calls out over the waves:

Lady Aphrodite—I honour you in all your names and dimensions:
Acidalia, Cytherea, Cerigo

Lady of Cyprus! Lady of Cythea!

Your body writhes and delights with dolphins, roses, doves, shells, scallops, sparrow and swan.

Your bed grinds with the pleasure of your men: Hephaistos, Ares, Dionysus, Hermes, Adonis, Poseidon, Anchisis.

We follow the whale's road south, but you send us on raven road north. This is not headway.

Why do you send our raft backwards? Why do bring me to an inlet of despair?

"Oi! Shh. It's inappropriate."

Is that her? It's coming from a little black girl crouched down by the other side of the door in pink trainers. She has three braids half way down her back and a T-shirt that says *Jamaica*. Far be it for the man to insist on a typical manifestation of the Goddess of Love. Next to her is a young man who seems oblivious to the raft's presence. But she is beckoning and pointing, but keeping her focus on the boy. The kid has woken up now too, and is looking blearily about. Trying unsuccessfully a few times, they get their craft tethered to an ancient iron pole jutting from the grey waters. They bob quietly about.

The boy, Darren, glances over to the young girl, "Tell us a story."

At this she smiles, "You are one. How old are you anyway? I've felt you before."

He looks out to sea, "Twenty-two. I know you too. A little. Every time I've felt something good. I've kipped out a couple of times. Never slept far from town. But I heard rooks, and saw thousands and thousands of stars. Worms in the dew, badger set in the woods. Saw a stag once, bending his head by a small stream. Christ. Such beauty. I felt crippled when I saw it, not free. Never knew that my ears rang till I heard that silence. It was awful. Like some enormous secret had been kept from me. I'm too damaged for you now."

His companion takes that in, and continues her questions, "What's your dad say about you going to prison? Mother?

He grunts: "Fuck knows. Don't know my mum. Not me real dad. He just took me on for money. He's like a ghost. Shiftless. Until he's on me with his hammer. Then he's wide awake, present and correct. Anyway, he had to leave the estate. He beat up Justin Peterson's dad, and when he got out of hospital he said that my dad had raped him too. The whole estate's after 'in now. They'll kill him.

Anyway. I like this. What's happening. Talking to you. It's like Dances With Wolves. Bloody hilarious. It's feudal where I come from. Concrete warrens you'd think no one would give a shit about. But we did. Not in a flowers and garden kind of way, but fierce.

Only way into the bigger gangs was to walk into their territories alone. No back up. Find out where the big man lived, or drank. Take to him with a crowbar or a brick. Let his people bring it upon you. Going down was no shame. The shame was not getting up again. Not taking it again and again.

First time I took it like that they threw me in front of car. Knuckle-duster to the head, then a wire brush, like what you clean shoes with. So beaten even my dad went quiet.

As I sat sucking baby food with a straw every day I looked over the town at the far hills. Wouldn't enter my head to go there. Or anyone's I knew. It was like a painting. If I touched it I'd tear the canvas. Like the set of the play. I never knew it breathed.

While I was in bed, a strange thing happened. Everyone seemed to leave. Pregnancies, jail, other gangs, bright lights of Didsbury. One day I looked out and everyone on my street was gone. Just me. A grown man in a fucking shell suit living with his dad and a hammer.

When I could walk, I went back. This time they let me walk all the way from the bus station to the swimming pool without so much as a blow. It was raining. I felt like a king.

I loved being in a gang. And it's time to get my stripes now. Do my time."

He becomes thoughtful now, starts rolling a cigarette.

"Will you be able to talk to me like this in prison? Reckon this door of the many locks will get in the way. Tell me a story."

She smiles, "I told you. You are a story."

But he won't let it go, "Tell me a story of someone like me then. Show me myself as I am to you."

At this she straightens. "I will. But I need to take something from you first."

She reaches into his jacket and pulls out the grey-green pebble.

"Close your eyes, Darren Holderly. It is time to take your innocence. But in exchange I give you a story worth the hearing."

The little black girl stands to her full, tiny height on Lost Boys' Rock and begins to speak.

✳✳✳

Wudu-Wasa

There is a chief of England who has in his territories a dismal swamp: pathless for every living thing. Like the sullen mind of a wolf, a fist of mud-water and witch-thorn. A place you go into and never come out. Beyond it, past the meres, salt marsh, the washes, far to the east is clear Nordic light, across the sea's trackways:

the green wave
the swan's road
the whale path

the realm of the Spear-Danes.

Seat of Bjornvig,
fiery Ragner,
deadly Sigurd.

But here? The east lands?
Swamp. Bilge. Fen.

The place where every bad dream goes to roost.

The ambitious chief orders exploration, has his thanes move slowly towards the centre from all four quarters. From a safe lid of turf, holy men offer prayerful encouragement and finger their beads and iron. In the centre of the moisture is the blue world's axis mundi, its genius loci.

Wudu-Wasa.
Wood-Wo.
Wild Man.

A vast man, sleek wet fur, one baleful eye in the centre of his forehead.

Witch of the bleak shore. Bound, he is taken from his home, from his wetness, into the dry appraisal of the chief. Chief locates something he didn't expect. Wealth is present. Proper wealth. Can't explain it, put his finger on it, but knows he is in the presence of something vast, unruly, and immensely rich.

The being will not speak. No persuasion, no torture, will bend him. He's a lonely bar of iron.

A cage is built, then a tower constructed of huge chunks of granite, lacking either love or grace. Tower is huge, blocking both the sun and the moon.

But at night, the watery being slops the chief's corridors, places his immense fingers into the murk of the leader's dreams, keeps him haggard with wondering. Called to war, the chief places the key to the cage in the lime-white hand of his wife. Roused by his stallion beneath him, he bellows a sentence of death to anyone who would think of freeing his shaggy guest.

Maybe on the battlefield he will be free of those dreams.

Wife keeps the keys in her pocket, night and day, will not be parted from them. How a wife fingers a husband's command, just to keep his memory close. She lights the yellow candle in the small window, keeps vigil.

They have one child, seven years old: a wit, a cherub, a cub in the yard, lively for mischief. A boy that likes to wander, and, whilst playing in the long grass, drops his golden apple, an apple that rolls past the guards, into the tower and through the bars of the iron cage.

The pup runs to the bars, and gazes in.

There is the being that never dries out.

A sopping fire, red-furred, like a slurried hill of foxes, and the one mournful eye.

The boy tries to barter for his apple, appeal to the goodness of the beast. He witnesses sound from the hairy lump, something no whip or jewel had been capable of procuring. Ah, the old arrangement between young boys and wild men.

You must steal the key
from your mother

open the innermost door

set me free.

The boy is not without guile. He runs to his mother and places his hot little head on her lap.

"Something is tickling my ear! Help!"

Mother peers into that delicate shell, the cherubic jug of sound, and spies nothing. Not even a spider.

But long enough for his hand to curl into her pocket and take the key. The betrayal takes only a second. And he is lamb-scampering back to the tall tower, drunk on the lark, a boy-god.

With the doors unlocked, the being finally stands, the cage shines with furry red light, the air moistens, shudders with crackling bursts of spasmed electrics.

He fixes the melancholy eye on the boy and gives him a whistle:

If you need me
blow it.

And he's gone into the tree line.

Gone gone
gone beyond.

Thin dawn light, and the cage is discovered empty. The key has been placed back in the mother's pocket, and much bewilderment ensues. All recall the chief's puffy pronouncement, and on arrival from the battle, his shape warps with fury.

His eyes twist and strain under their lids, thigh bones grind knee sockets like mortar and pestle, curls spit lightning that scatter all but the hardiest of thanes.

All the toys thrown from the pram.

When the boy sees blame fly up towards his mother he speaks, appropriately, truly. The father cannot take the life of his son, even if the people scorn the weakness, has him driven deep into the grey slag of the wild swamp. And he a boy of seven.

The warriors prod the bubbling sod till they will go no further, draw crosses on their bread, throw the bones on slate and see they have entered unholy waters. It is dusk as they leave the little one.

He sleeps that night in the branches of a tree, and in the shivering morning remembers the Wudu-Wasa's whistle.

He blew and it came.

As if out of the ground,
a great shuddering lump
sloughed with water—
the source of all rivers,
the tears in every eye,
the mighty current,
the true drop.

Come get up on my back.

Not needing an invitation twice, the boy leapt from the tree onto the confirming shoulders of the beast.

Little hands find ruddy cords of hair like rope or binding vine, to keep him secure as the beast-man starts to lope further and further into the ward. Deeper and stranger and darker, till of a sudden the two sink beneath the waters, the silt, the mud, the rough grasses.

A crow's wing
is wrapped around
the boy

mouth ears nose
fill with black sound and dark water
a churning sound   a hundred wild geese
amok   loose over ocean

And then he can breath again,
behold again.

Down below is a kingdom.

Below the waters
is a mead-hall:
kegs, storytellers, servants,
meadows, wild horses,
intricate walled gardens.

This is the residence of
the one-eyed-man.

This?

Seven years he trains the boy, firms his calves, sharpens his wit with spear and blade and axe, shows him how to swim with a dagger between his teeth. By fourteen he can pass for eighteen. Limber, agile, elegant in speech: ready for the world's unfolding.

The rusty man takes him to a holy stream where he bathes his head. When he lifts his wet curls, they gleam like tempered gold. Plainly dressed, the boy clambers for one last time onto the wild man's back, swimming up and into merry Angle-land, breaking a bubbling cold surface.

All night he runs, Wudu-Wasa, the ruddy bear, fire-spark under moon, till at dawn he slowly places the lad down on firm soil.

Take humble work keep your gold hair under your hat speak not of your origins.
If you need something I possess hold it firm in your thinking.

He takes work with a powerful chief as an apprentice garden boy. When queried about his hat, he claims a scurvy has robbed him of his locks, made him bald as a butcher's arse. Such an image quells curiosity.

It also keeps him far from luxury. Has him camped in the outhouse, on thin straw, a companion to northern cattle, the golden murmurs of beehives. He is not constructed to complain, and enjoys seasonal buffeting, the thorn-ripped hands, rich black soil under rake, planting to the movement of the moon.

If he slacks a little in his duties he can simply *wish* the job finished, and soon it is, the dark field ploughed, wild herbs gathered. He becomes invaluable.

A third daughter of the chief glimpses an early dawn through the beeches, but when she peers through the bough again, sees it's the glowing locks of the boy's hair, being washed in the salmon-silver river.

She resolves to have him.

The other sisters mock the bald-headed servant, thinking it a right hoot—their sister's blushing affection. But she had beheld what they never could. She treats the bombast of her father's scolds as puffs of distant cloud, scudding briefly past that beloved sun.

Oh daddy, *please.*

A tournament is prepared, the usual terms: three days of combat, the greatest warrior receives a golden apple and the hand of the daughter of the chief.

For two days the gardener comes in disguise, the first day riding a horse as red as wine, the second day a coal-black steed, and the third a milk-white stallion, golden hair streaming.

He wins all three bouts and tosses the first two apples to robust young warriors but keeps the third. That is for the third daughter. When the commoner arrives with the apple, the chief steams with rage, declares he has stolen it from the white warrior, spends several nights by the gate waiting up for the valiant hero.

Finally, sourly, he accepts that love's clear wine moves between the gardener and his daughter. A hunt is arranged for the three suitors.

In the spirit of humiliation, the gardener is furnished with a grey donkey, whilst the other two hate-gaze from heavy horses. They admire their reflections in still pools, gaze wonderingly at their own beauty, whilst the runt shuffles behind.

At the edges of the kingdom there is a clear divide: verdant forest—dark swamp. The two suitors canter into the emerald bough, and the gardener takes to the marshes, popping and sizzling.

But come dusk it is his nag laden down with hare, fox, and even wild boar. The laughing boys of the forest had found nothing, not even a rabbit.

Their tone becomes flattering, even pleading to save face and share the caught game. He gives it all, in exchange for their apples. Next day a hunt, next day the same bounty for the gardener. In the half-light the warrior's vast moustaches droop.

This time he demands a strip of flesh from each of the men, in a place hidden from sight—then the grouse and stag would be theirs.

They wince, agree, endure.

That night wicks are lit, and the rushes lain for feast. Bronze on arm, fawn cloak, keg uncorked, the gloeman's harp, hounds at his feet. But chop has not greased lip, red beer not whetted beard before news scorched the merriment, cindered the joy. The sea-wolves, north men were that very night setting rampant ruckus to the east coast of England's shore.

Over the meres
   mud flats silt
salt marshes lug worm
   the deep wash

everything was on fire

the call to battle
the call to battle
the call to battle

Sound horn,
hound howl,
clatter of chain mail,
dull thunk of shield
then out of the womb-hall
into cold black winds
of un-calm.

Rook caws the coming slaughter.

Woden turns suddenly on the hill.

Reluctantly slink the suitors. Eager, but slowed by the donkey, is the gardener, waving his pitchfork.

The swiftest way to the coast is by a lonely peat-marsh. Of a sudden, the suitors pull back from the bearded warriors and round on the donkey man, set upon him, punch his face, smash his groin, jab his kidneys, push him into the slipperiness of the wastes, let the porridge grey mud suck dark tight round donkey's hoofs, watch the man's panic as he loses his grip on this world.

Pitch black sound fills his ears.

The suitors grin lupine—no awkward talk now of missing apples, or strips of flesh off their rumps. They trot leisurely to battle, moustaches waxed and splendid.

Under a cuticle of moon time passes
the bog bubbles, turns slow thoughts,

glints and wisps and muddy murmurs.

An eruption, a casting out, a crust-mud slashing
from which bursts a white horse   a golden rider

A rider thundering occult paths, who reaches the coastal battle as the chief ails under Norse might, who gives himself entirely to the fight—all skill—all ambition—all silver slashing sword—all swamp education roaring its underworld bellow through the lion's blood of his veins.

He is magnificent on the claret beach, a glowing prism of hope to the scattered Angles. He alone with the cattle of his fists reaches into sullen northern waters, by sheer will tips the dragon-boats back down the whale-road they come from.

In his vast spasm
the Norse-bandits flee   they flee
into the sea's foaming sperm.

Holy Christ. The chief has never seen such a victory.

White Warrior is carried on the backs of the men
to the mead-hall. They sing low
through the rising light
in a gentle scattering of rain.

It doesn't get any better.

Pyres will be made for the many dead.

Early morning, the feast roars back into life. Chop on plate, mead in cup, hound by heel, scars to boast. A dizzying affair. The chief asks the White Warrior to reveal his face. When he beholds the gardener he bends his head with shame.

He produces the golden apple as proof of his surety. Then also the golden apple that rolled into the Marsh Man's cage so many years ago. Engraved is his name and status. The chief turns, eager for similar magic from the other suitors. They seem locked in pale conversation, and, when confronted, have not the apples.

Shame will scatter them to the crosswinds when the gardener produces the apples they were so swift to cast off for a little pheasant.

And so, a man who learnt to swim with a dagger between his teeth, and a woman that could behold gold, become the true Inner-King and Queen of England. To this day their feast continues, in the hill inside the hill.

We see this

as through a dark glass,

but we see it

*** * ***

The little black girl stops and peers across at Darren. He's snoring softly against the door. She sighs, and hopes he got at least halfway through. She casts one quick glance at the two listeners and is gone. Soon there will be the sound of the keys in the door and hands will take Darren into his keep.

The little girl turns to the man on the raft and gestures to his pocket. He knows what she wants. She speaks, "I am blowing a story of weight into your days. Of heft. I am still whittling you. Still frying your edges in my pan.

Now give me the royal trade for such experience. Didn't you want the Song of the Sirens? That is not a sound for a naive child."

The man walks to the edge of the raft and pulls from his pocket a grey-green stone.

He throws it to the girl, and she catches it, the way it's always been done.

*** * ***

The man of the Underneath wonders if he believes in full—beginning to end—stories anymore. We seem to be tossed from scene to scene, in an impenetrable order. He won't say this to his daughter, but he thinks it.

Her questions come: *Where was the love story Dad? Where do I need to steal the key from? Do girls get to meet kind, swampy wild men too? What's the warrior stuff about? And monsters, how do you deal with monsters?*

He rattles a thought round in his head, and tries to respond, "I often get monsters waking me up in the middle of the night; it's hard. But I get up, brew a little coffee and give them something like a story or a poem. Something as dark as them, that's the thing. Pushback. They see my teeth glinting in the moonlight. It's their invitation to the feast. They need to taste themselves in our words otherwise they don't believe us, otherwise they are still out there watching from the tree line. And when we can only half-glimpse them then they become more terrible because our imagination then becomes a kind of black magic of awful possibility. I can't say this works as a salve, or quite sends them off happy. But it's maintenance work, ritual work—it's what my man Finn MacColl calls 'the music of what is'. You know about Finn, don't you?"

She groans, "Yes Dad."

His look of concern lessens. "Well, thank god for that. Anyway. Monsters. They sit there, I sit there, but now this third thing sits between us. Maybe it's art, maybe it's a small black loaf for them to eat. Maybe like Psyche, I am sorting through piles of grain in the half-light.

Why am I doing this? Because in a few hours I will have to get up, make breakfast, somehow find a uniform from the bottom of the wash pile, pay bills, and drive the lanes to the school gates. Got to get you to school kid.

We've got kingdoms to maintain, all of us, but there in the middle of the night is when I have to give the monsters their counsel. If I do all the outer-stuff without some kind of mediation they flood me, devour me, annihilate me. And I can't indulge that too often.

Sometimes it's time to be tough. For some folk, it can be grievous when we have to really learn the art of defending something we love in a fierce and sustained manner. To kick ass. Repeatedly.

Comes a time we all have to defend something.

You have to enter the terrain of the Warrior—in a man or woman (by all means find another phrase if you want kiddo). Endurance, strategy, even those most spiritually unfashionable of elements; goals and a plan (mutable though it may have to be). You have to dig in, be savvy, protect yourself, learn how to be a scrapper—temporarily override the Lover in you that wants comfort and more chocolate, or the Hermit that wants to withdraw with her books and fireplace and hanging herbs and dozing hound.

Sometimes, mercifully not always, life requires you to take to the battlefield. You are called to war. And to survive that, you need to be around those that know something about it.

It's the warrior that accepts the fate they are given, but then brings all their ingenuity, power and flat out tenacity to forge a destiny from that lump of fate that got dished to them. Destiny we have a little say about. As grown ups, destiny comes from our response, our faithfulness to a longer arc of unfolding than just the bad news that plonks into our lap. That's not the end of the story.

Not to the warrior. Not to Boudicca, Crazy Horse, Rosa Parks. We get to renegotiate some terms, and sometimes for that we need a great river of sustained strength. But we also choose our battles carefully, what to surrender and what to stake our staff in the ground for."

The two of them cuddle a little closer.

"Y'know, I've been thinking about Athena—she's the Goddess of battle strategy—literally burst armoured into this world from an axe blow to the side of Zeus's head. What do we birth from that kind of attack? (for Zeus this shows up when he has the mother of all headaches). She is the only Olympian Goddess that we see again and again in armour; shield on arm, spear in hand, helmeted but visor open to reveal her radiance. She carries great bundles of owl energy; a wisdom that is far-sighted, helping her to fly through the darkest of nights. She has a harness on both her passions and her fears—in fact it's claimed she invented the bridle, the yoke and the chariot.

She blesses you with iron spine when caught in paranoia and attack. She gifts you steadiness, tenacity, strategy and a focus on results. She's not a dreamer, or a grief woman, but it is she that gives Perseus the idea to gaze at Medusa via a shield and not directly and so be turned to stone. She opens a road of deflecting intensities and steadying imagination. And sometimes the imagination needs steadying.

She's in the business of winning. She is not so much about relatedness and connection (we can go somewhere else for that, remember we're on the battlefield), she will keep you in touch with the 'bottom line' of a situation instead of being naive. She instructs you not to just live emotionally moment by moment but, as a Goddess of weaving, to methodically and diligently, row upon row, thread what you want from the ground up.

She's like a medieval walled garden rather than wilderness. She's different from Artemis. When chaos bangs at the boundaries, she offers the structure to build cosmos—and fashion boundaries, and value stamina and planning as well as inspiration and creativity. She wants to teach form, and to actually demonstrate there are times to not take everything so devastatingly personally.

Why? So you can maintain just enough sacred distance to have some objectivity under intense attack. Sacred distance can save you when surrounded by swords.

God knows kid, the Olympians are a complicated bunch, to have Athena as the only guiding energy long term provokes all sorts of problems, but when we are facing combat, and an overview, she is a temple to serve in. Service includes getting educated about your enemies' ambitions, curbing paranoias, not indulging whimsy, knowing when to put the armour on, when to cut, when to show mercy, who your true allies are. She is one who speaks quietly in your ear, enables you to think clearly in the midst of big emotional struggles. She will carry a lantern for you.

And, when the battle is done, remember, remember to remove that armour, bathe in milk, call down the sweetness of Demeter to welcome you, my darling Shield-Maiden back into the place of corn, and laughter, warmth and restoration. It's coming, I promise."

She half sighs, half groans. "I believe you Dad. Thousands wouldn't."

Dad's hands are salmon pink from bailing water, and he needs the tale to work on his bones too. Something in the story has made him broody and he says little now. There was love a plenty in the story, but maybe not the kind he'd like to glimpse, at least one more time before they throw him in the clay.

Quietly, they are both missing the little boat full of gypsies and emigres. These big stories are like visiting the Grand Canyon over and over, after a while you want something more intimate, smaller—you want less.

They stay warm together on the raft, and cheer each other up with talk of Greece: she's never been. Maybe Leonard Cohen never died at all, and they could visit him at his little house on Hydra. He'll be drinking Raki on the porch with Jaqueline Du Pre and Robert Graves. For sure.

They feast on cold lamb and greens, and share a bottle of sparkling water to feel exotic. As they fall asleep, the man glimpses tall male figures, powerful but indistinct, walking over the waves, with young boys on their shoulders.

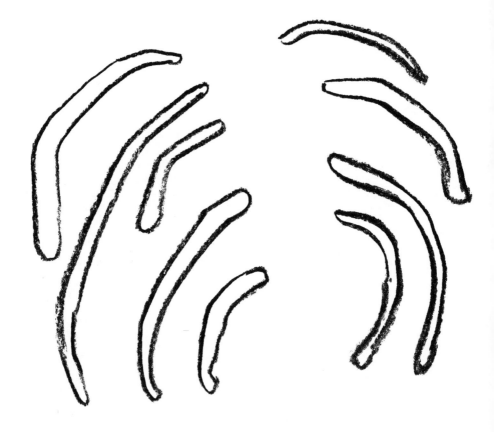

Chapter Ten

Bone Memory

On the raft and filled with thought.

Love and memory.

What is it in love that forces us to travel backwards? Backwards into our nostalgias, reveries, childhood manias, and ancestral paranoias? We don't flee what came before, but fly exactly into its snapping teeth. We are not composed but undone, not solidified but loosened. We are a house of agitated birds flying in and out of time.

That's how he writes his books, by becoming agitated. Un-domestic.

He walks round and round the very edges of his imagination with a lantern finding all those lonely little gleams of light, those furry animals of the unconscious that want to come on board. Never abandons them.

In middle age he's been thinking more and more about memory. He's been thinking that there must be different kinds. There's the sort that you can trace back to a certain age and then present rather like a C.V., like peering through ice. It provokes no great pathos, just a four-square stomp through the years. A checklist. It's not without its uses. We could call this skin memory. Pops up at job interviews. Reveals a mind not ravaged by substance abuse. Skin memory hovers like a hawk over the creek of our own years. We need skin memory, especially its emotional distance.

Then there's another kind. In this squats a greater sense of the interior: your wider senses lurch into range—you can *feel* the deathly cool of the telephone in your hand as your lover breaks faith with you, the reek of the phonebox (a scent you have become almost fond of as you associate it with your nightly attempts at courting) and the crazy weight of the dark as you stagger out into that fresh March night of 1989. Now that recollection is quite a different animal to the first. That shoots the hawk right out of the sky. Gets these adrenals moving. Shirt sticky on the back. First love memories have a little more boom and clatter—either that or they are placed well and truly in the deep freeze. So it's all a little more holistic, edgier, a flesh memory.

But over many years now as a storyteller he's found there's another kind again. Bone memory. The kind that got him on the raft in the first place.

This is the tears unbidden, the clench of the gut, the wild-sky-waking of some story that lashes its great sexy tail straight round the table legs of your steady life and pulls all the crockery to the floor. And you bend your head and thank it for the trouble. Alive alive-oh. Amen the thunderbolt in the dark void.

It's as if in the dust of your collagen and calcium is a secretion of alchemical deposits that can't be readily accounted for in the push-pull of your years. It's not to do with a Lincolnshire high school, or a leery husband or anything you really can claim to have experienced, it doesn't quite add up. Where did it come from? Be sure, it has spook attached. But you've always sensed it at the edge of your vision. Maybe you don't talk about it. Maybe as a child, just before sleep, with your eyes closed you beheld hundreds of faces you've never met. Remember that? Who are they and where do they come from? If someone tries to explain them away, it's vital you tell them they're an idiot.

But what is this terrible treasury, so magnificent and elusive? Is bone memory the way into a religious life that we are not supposed to believe in anymore? Why does a chick raised in a laboratory shudder when the cardboard shape of a hawk swoops its shadow over the babe, despite never being in the presence of a predator?

The greatest storytellers curate echoes.

They can feel them in ancient stories, and if there's no echo, no stirring of bone memory, then they won't tell them. But if the echo trembles its blue bell in the teller, then their work has begun. This isn't as simple as maintaining that a moment in the story is a metaphor for something that happened when you were six. That's a cop out if that's where the enquiry ends. This is *participation mystique*. This is a time-wrestle; when as a teller you know things you should not know, bear witness to the moment where the horses of past, present and future all drink from the deep trough which is the story being told in its ordinary and tremendous fullness. You commence holy seance with trees and saints and croft. You change your shape. If that sounds grandiose then you've understood exactly what I'm trying to communicate. A great time-wrestler will push you out of the normal range of reference without for a moment belittling the lived human experience; they will render you completely to its vastness.

He knows what he's thinking lacks some connecting tissue, allows a degree of misrule into what's presented. So he tries to come at it again. We have the general recollections of a life, then we have the deeper, more emotive reservoirs—the endings, the betrayals, the happiness, and then we have chthonic memory and from that erupts the word *soul*. And he does mean erupt. You respond to certain wild views, grand old castles, the delicate swoop of the goldfinch. You walk into a Finnish church and you stop still. You know you've been there before. But not this time round.

It is, some would say, a little baffling. Maybe once in every hundred years or so you may meet someone who has the same subterranean pressure points as you, but it's as rare as the white-skinned deer in a far Northern forest that the hunter weeps for when he takes its life. You and they share bone memory somehow.

Maybe that is what a soul-mate actually is. A bone-mate.

The passport to a modern life is often to drift through *without* the difficulty of such an encounter. But that passport becomes wretched when we realise that those very difficulties and their bullish prickles remind us that we are not alone. We aren't designed to do this alone, no matter what they say. We're not here to glide through. It's a contact sport.

All these crazy folktales, myths and fairy tales are a way of strengthening your capacity to vocalise bone memory; to evoke not just pastoral but prophetic information. To reach back into history and realise it was riding alongside you all the time. You just had to reach over and touch its bridle. A way of becoming proficient at your particular form of echolocation. This must not be kept entirely in the hand of the specialist anymore: the times are far too pressing. To have the capacity to not just carry but *communicate* bone memory is a talismanic activism against forces that do not wish you well. And yes, they're out there.

He knows chaos stands at the gate of this statement, he knows that. Not much he can do about it. Licence for every eye-quivering mystic and low grade channeller for a thousand miles to bellow their celestial reports uninvited into your weary face. Sorry about that.

Another place where many feel bone memory is the living world. Certain places just evoke reverie: the rooks grumpy atop a fenland marsh, the grey-glitter curves of a Welsh estuary. It's always been that way for him too. To walk in the cool of the day in the valley of your fathers. To stand, chest deep in its song-line, and behold how a stretch of land receives its own ancient tales. How does it speak back?

What could it look like to wander, in this mid-life time, into the hidden lays of

Britain? Its dream-psyche? Whatever it has left in times like these. Whatever is not anaesthetised, splayed on the rack of hallucinatory progress, or hitching a grumpy lift to the outer Hebrides. What does this humped and shingled, chalked and bullish animal have to growl? Could we still walk out one mid-summer morning— stroll a verdant motorway overcome by weed-flower that shrinks to a crumbling A-road, then onwards to a green lane, to a medieval cart track, to the tiny glistening hoof prints of a roebuck. Could such a consecration still take place? Such a holy diminishment? Can we move into the righteous and magnificent enchantments of Britain's gramarye? How dare we?

What do these strange, burning wheels of story have to disclose?

But where were we? Memory. That thing so vital to a storyteller. That clouded buff of image that you plead to, pray to, to crowd into your jaw and then be loosened into the world like a scent we'd almost given up ever catching again. You have to enchant the story to come as much as the audience that receives it.

But reader, he has a confession.

It's memory that flees him as he sits in the green room of a Manhattan night club, or stands in frosty-dark outside a Dorset longhouse as he prepares to speak. It goes away. Always. There's no memory at that moment. Or at least not the flesh kind. Or even the body. Just blankness. A kind of weakness too. He feels unsubstantial. There's no A to B, no recital, no incantation, just a kind of nothing. It's not a good sensation. Only prayers to gird the way at that moment. Then, sure enough, someone emerges from the dark and says its time.

You glance around but there's no spirit-companions. Nada. Just some bad coffee and an article on Rimbaud stuffed down the back of the sofa. So be it. So you stand up and shake yourself down, snorting like some Shetland pony still waiting for its load. And somewhere out there, under the lights, that little pony will have to become a lion. The stories won't show up for less. And then, and only then, as you croak your greetings to the murky strangers does bone memory show up. Pushes all the other gradients of recollection aside and speaks its rough-rattle of beauty to the second, secret heart of those gathered listeners.

High risk strategy, circus work really—tightrope, no net.
He scribbles something down.

Note to self: *Lion Tamer Knows He Needs To Become Lion.*

PART THREE

Chapter Eleven

Spirit Bear and the Bleak Shore

Swish Swish Swish. North North North.

The duo of the raft have been practising West Country wind magic: tying knots in rope to manipulate the air, hurling coin and words over the side of the raft.

But all it seems to do is encourage mischief, and the wind—flattered—has merrily picked up its pace, taking them up to the islands of Britain's far north, amongst the Knarstons, Thorfinns and Mucklehaas.

Where a scattering of stars meets creels of lobsters and the kestrel road, where the seal-proud coast meets wind-bent grasses, and just off the beach, a twinkle of a tavern, a candle in every window. They are not too proud to row towards it.

Soon their jeans are fringed with sand and salt, as they trudge their way up to the inn, a bag of washing slung over the man's shoulder. A descending cold hurries them along, and they dimly notice it is autumn. There's a sluice of fallen leaves on the path.

The snug is low lit, and soon fish pie is on plate for the two famished travellers, stout in glass for the older, a lemonade for the younger. Other than a radio quietly transmitting the shipping forecast and the date, it could be any time in the last seventy years. Three women seem to run the place, and have an easy way about them. Silver hair, even the youngest, in her twenties.

When the man next looks up, his daughter is in conversation with them, he thinks she's talking about the washing. A few minutes later she's back:

"They have a room for tonight, and hot water for washing and a bath. They've offered to take me for a walk on the beach, tell me about the place. Women's stuff. Can I go Dad? *Please?*"

Dad winces a little, letting the kid go when they have just washed up in such a desolate place, but the women seem solid, if a touch otherworldly. Sure, sure. But be back by dusk at the very latest O.K? To his surprise, all three women leave with her, and a cherubic gent soon appears from the cellar and takes over behind the bar.

A half it is, and a healthy gulp of island whisky.

The man who knows about the Underneath starts to detect a conversation happening a few tables away, and gets the same familiar prickle he had when he heard the wind talking to the woman on the beach, or the small girl talking to the prisoner. It's the feeling that there's something being said that he has to hear, that is being spoken to him. And that's a West Country accent right there. You are sent by the wind a thousand miles north, and it's a West Country accent? To hear such a voice so far from home, so fulsome and deep lived, causes tears to prick the man's eyes.

There is a bushy black beast in the corner of the tavern. Only just a man. Smells distinctly of autumn and ciggies and Sundays counting the hard cards of grief. As if such a thing had a scent, and yes, you know it does. There's a younger man, rather earnest, talking to him.

Even though he is absolutely not allowed to do so, the being—whose name is Croc—sits and starts thoughtfully to roll a cigarette, lays out the papers and tobacco. Starts singing:

Awake you pretty maids awake
refreshed from drowsy dream
and haste to the dairy house
for us a dish of cream

If not a dish of yellow cream
then give us kisses three
the woodland bower is
white with flower
and green is every tree

The life of man is but a span
he blossoms as a flower
he makes no stay is here today
and vanished in a hour

and vanished in a hour

He grinds his fulsome croon to a swift death behind the barn, and turns to his drinking companion, Magnus. He asks, "You ever felt mighty Magnus?

Properly solid?

It's infectious. People sense it. And when it leaves they sense that too. It's like mercury. Then they follow some other poor bastard. C'mon boy, sing some lines with me, it'll clear up your spots. Your father's father's father has his arm round his father and they are singing with us:

If not a dish of yellow cream
then give us kisses three
the woodland bower is
white with flower
and green is every tree"

Magnus recoils, "Can't. It's sexist."

Croc smiles and pretends to mishear, "Sexy? It is. Very. Called courting boy. No drug in drink, no heavy hands, just a man reaching out and finding himself in the budding elm and the lightning storm. Man not afraid to have some flavour, some depth. That's what makes us mighty. You know the word *Yarak?*"

Magnus shrugs, "No."

Croc gathers himself, "The supreme readiness of a hawk as it prepares to hunt. Shape-changer. Huge breasted, fire-eyed, unutterable grandeur. Even frigging god bows before hawk at this moment. Yarak.

Why boy, you don't have any. Not a drop. There is a deficit. You ever taken it to the cobbles Magnus? Ever lit a man up?"

Magnus's silent.

"Ever woken to your blood on the pillow? Ever stood alone and unsupported outside the chippy at ten o'clock on a Saturday night with some twat from the next village hammering on your skull? Defining moments. Tribal. Old. Woman likes to see a man shake his tail feather every now and then, have a fucking opinion. *No.* You're a coat holder aren't you boy? So in some deep way you can't quite trust yourself. You're a geld. Women smell it. You ain't been in the trenches boy."

At this Magnus flushes, and gives a little pushback. "Don't shame me. Fine coming from you Croc. Not exactly the Don Juan of Orkney are you? Not laying waste to Hamnavoe with your charm. No quim in your cave. No. You're just a strange old man who rings at the church. Who speaks riddles in The Swan's Road that no one believes. No one even knows where you live."

Croc continues to roll.

Magnus tries again, "I heard more. A shrink. That you went mental at the fayre, tore down a marquee, drove Bjorn's cattle out of the top field, tried to kidnap old Margie Sigurd in a wheel barrow and ravage her, punched that young lad from the mainland in the face. Lost a tooth. That you have to go and see a shrink since then."

Croc gives an expansive smile and spreads his arms, "Ah, well that ain't me you see. There's this other one. The summer one. As wild as I am wise. The great loosener. The shit-kicker. The proper dose. It were him. As it happens I'm giving up that face tonight, settling into my wintering. That was him giving you grief just then. What do they call it? I'm *transitioning*. Time was, there'd be a way of containing his antics, making 'em beautiful, giving 'em form. That gone, it's just an old man at a party waving his antlers at toddlers. Grim. I used to eat 'em. Toddlers that is."

At this Magnus almost spills his pint. "Convenient. So you're the innocent are you Croc? This is called multiple personality disorder—major health issue Croc. Major."

The whole affair is heating up, and Croc shifts a little, while still trying to light his roll up. "Personality? You stupid shit. I'm talking about a god. A god who burns up your bloodstream, calls down the lightning, is the sap in every plant. I'm talking about the wild hunt. Who they used to called The Big Knife. I don't have multiple personality disorder, I have multiple *god* disorder.

That shrink is wrong. He tries to make things small. Reduce 'em. Says I didn't sow enough wild oats as a youth, so I made him up to act it out. That's woeful thinking boy. How will the barley sway without the gods, how will the brown trout find the source? Cutting the world to pieces with his thinking that shrink. His office is more dangerous than me riding Bjorn's cattle into the creche. Which I can neither confirm nor deny. Anyway, enough of this banter. Least I get out and about. You shy boy? That why you hide in a tower? That your idea of socialising?"

Magnus nods, "I suppose it is. Yep. Tower is where I first had ale."

Croc raises one eyebrow. Surprising as it may sound, Croc and Magnus are bell ringers.

"Don't look surprised, it was you that gave it to me. 13. Nutty, dark, a wizard's potion, nectar from under the wing of a Goshawk. I'd never known you lot had a keg stashed away up there. It was Christmas Eve. Quite a moment for me. I'd trudged over the fields from my parents' house to get to you. Taken such persuading to join the ringers. What with the reputation."

Croc nods, "Quite. That thing with the milk churn and the goat and the priest. That was wrong. We shouldn't of done that."

But by now Magnus is in a reverie. "Field ridged with frost. Sun behind a flank of grey. Three rookeries on the northern side—always used to count them. Getting dark. As I walked I could see the sky changing, that strange grey-yellow that promises snow.

And then suddenly I'm knocking on the tower door and you let me in. *You let me in.* The secret society. Murdo, Grettir, Raglan, Thorvald, Harald and yourself. Grinning men in the dark. Handsome gargoyles. Ancient. Steam from your jaws, candles lit. And you were friendly too: kind, not harsh like I fretted about.

You even sat me down for half an hour, told me some history. *Campanologia.* That was what you called it. The noble art of ringing bells. Gave me dozens of methods: Grandsire Method and Stedman's principle. Told me stories of the great towers of the south: Lincoln, Canterbury, Norfolk, London and the men that worked them. Made me dizzy. Like I was touching something deep and underground in me. A river underneath my own short life. Like I was growing feathers."

Croc is touched, and briefly pats the young man's arm. "That's nice lad, keep going."

Magnus gathers himself, "We rang for the Carol service and then we went to the pub before Midnight Mass. I felt like a prince of the lanes. Shoulder to shoulder with pirates, highwaymen, shaggy men of god. You took me to the Nobody Inn and gave me a little whisky. Just a little mind. But to me it was a pint. I loved you that night Croc. For your kindness and your fierceness. Like a king amongst the oestrogen.

You even gave me a little book, I still have it somewhere. *Tintinnalogia.* 1668. Duckworth and Stedman. Yes! I still remember. And you gave me the chant. To remember when my shoulders ached. When I wanted to stop. Of those wild Suffolk boys who rang for six hours, ablaze with belling. Over 10,000 changes.

Look, I still know it:

On the 16th March, these bells they were swung
Such a peal in old England as never was rung
By any eight persons, indeed at one time
And now they are jolly and just in their prime
Little Spalding the carpenter not very stout
Took hold of the treble and swung her about
There was Sawyer the whittler he droops as he goes
Will start for the second as I do suppose
Wright the wethersett miller he's not very old
Yet he'd rather be ringing than taking of toll
There's Pettitt the blacksmith you very well know
He'll pull down the fourth and give her a good blow
There's Abbot the fifth, tho' young at his strokes
He'd rather be ringing than driving of spokes"

The two men do a little informal, archaic jig.

Magnus settles down again, but is visibly moved. "It's why I ring Croc. Where it takes me. The swing of the rope. I see all the things they've announced: the yard stiff with dead; marriages: the farmer's dark sons and the miller's daughters, babies getting their heads splashed, even a peal for a condemned man.

And when we're deep into the ringing, even that goes away Croc. Melodious trance. Back in the cave. Torchlight, antelope robes. That's what the tower is. Singing our little sound out towards the skylark and the wolf and the dragonfly and the elk. Before all the noise we fill the world with now. Something more wonderful.

A true offering, not an imposition. When we've finished I feel clean. Washed over. And behind me are other ringers, and behind them still more. I think the bells aren't quite Christian and aren't quite pagan anymore. No one believes in god OR the gods anymore, so they've bloody teamed up. We are a sound of the land singing back to itself."

Croc listens, and nods. Standing, he gestures towards the barkeep. "Tumnus! Another ale for all here gathered in this room at the top of the world. Magnus, for your story I give you a story, in the ancient way of trade: as the Vikings did with the Picts did with the Gaels did with the Moors did with the Arabs."

Croc is standing upright
Fire is leaping in the grate
Beer is frothing in the mug

The room darkens and tunes itself for the telling. Animals turn in their straw in the lonely hillside farms, even the arriving rain aims her drops in his direction. The teller's tone is ornate and formal, like the Beowulf singer, calling all to attention. He chews on his words like meat.

✳✳✳

Bleak Shore

Listen!

High islands swill with bright danger. Waves shudder, a crippling of bruised foam grinds its teeth in yolk-gold air, crests of wolf-fish drag kirkyard stones, and otter's fur, all the knives in a tinker's belt, down, down to the indigo deep.

We are north.

The settlement holds twenty huts. Fisherfolk still kin to the fairy, and the mer-people. The big man of the tribe holds firm to the old negotiations with the courts of sea and air. At the tree line he makes libation; he bends his head and cries when the Gentry croon, when the sparking lights come from the gloaming. Before time became a flying arrow, the fairy had gifted the beings of the sea—

They gave a merman a belt of seaweed, lathered thick with protections, which in turn blessed the croft. With the gift, the merman would know when the seas were stiff with herring, and would magic the tippled waves

Red
Green
White

He would send a message to the folks who would push their crafts into the spray.

The joy of the merman is to squat on a rock under the sun and see the men with their gathered nets: the lads knee deep in the twisting fish; boys fierce with living, chanting their hymnals. With his blessing from fairies, he can also bless.

Round the croft is a wind-crooked forest, ghoulish and fur-flanked, residence to bleak spirits, host to the unruly, and is a direction to which the settlement rarely turns. Watching all this good will is a black hag, a witch. Close to her side, a small, brown man—her familiar. She coos for that mighty belt, desires it. Bending herself to power she shudders enough magic into the brown man that he becomes a bee, a bee sweet-drunk with poison that then flew to the merman.

When the sting is delivered, it flows through scale and brine and muscle and the bee hefts the merman back to the hag's den. Strange but true. She produces a potion and feeds it to the merman. His body lurches into smoke and in an old copper pot she binds him, has it rowed miles off shore, and hurled into blue lobster dark.

Now she has the belt she does not care for it. A trinket.

The belt is gifted to the small brown man, who twists its powers for the gathering of gold.

It is hard time now for the people. The full summer of their nets are now gone; they splash around in the spray like lonely children.

The fish have acquired new genius for avoidance, aquatic strategies. Bellies are stuck to spines. Men take greater risks, come unstuck. Candles are snuffed, there is grief everywhere.

In time, a council is arranged between fairy and people. Winter beats its stuttering drum; frost stiffens the old man's cloak. Survival without fish is unlikely. At black quilled trees, the Fairy Queen walks with the chief.

The queen informs him that to get close to the witch and her accomplice, he must chuck his human reek. That a bear wears a scent more tuned to the forest, so shaggy-backed he must be if ever to reclaim the belt, if ever to find the merman.

She speaks old words to him, words that make him hurt, like he is sick, tight-bellied with dark berries. Then he is face down in the stubbled grasses, eating dirt, muscles spliced and expanded, flank flared thick with a coating of wiry black hair, snouted and hook toothed.

He is becoming Bear.

This is a Norse magic, an earth-secret hid drum tight in the fjords, in the bare stumped horizon and the bronze-sunned darkness of the far north—

That a human can be become an animal
and an animal a human.

Changeling.

Through that winter he stays loyal to his shape, catching only glimpses of the small man, a muscled bundle in the distance, close to the ground; pressing gold into the wet green crag that contains his swag. But, carrying the belt, he is too mighty to attack.

So Bear learns the lonesome dance of waiting, out there on the wooded crest, locked out from the bay of lights.

✳✳✳

One night, months into his suffering he appears at the hut of his beloved.

He paws the door, and the woman's old mother gazes out into the dark
and knows exactly who it is.

They let him in;
        his love shakes the flakes
                from his dark fur

and settles him by the fire to rest. Some small reprieve from his paw-numbed circling of the woods. He laps whisky and milk, moves into fuzzy half-dreaming, caught between the agile language of humans, and the fur-bellied mysteries of his new shape. For just a little while.

In the morning he pads out again, but this bolt-hole of the human remains, through the dead of the wintering year: the brushing of snow from the black fur, the dreaming fire, the brief nesting in the coo words of his sweet.

Spring comes, and Bear spots the witch's familiar fishing for salmon, beltless. He has him.

He strikes with all the music of violence—splays the little man, raw and sleek and pink left as a gifting to Raven. The black sisters conk and stir from Galloway to the reeky streets of London. Rooks caw a dark strip down Albion's back. Bear thrashes back into human shape, compressed and expanded, torn-a-shake, wetted by fairy, until he stands two-legged and blinking. The very air changes and the queen is there.

She gifts him arrow and bow and instruction to the witch's hut. Bear-shape or not, he is expected. The hag's dispatching is swift, not without pleading.

Her claims fall loose round him, loose like autumn leaves. The tribe is alert now, gaunt and dull eyed, but waking from their gnashing winter.

They gather by grey water. The Fairy Queen issues instruction to gird a boat, just a half mile into the slosh, where they would find a rusty crimson circle clear in the waves. To reach down and see what they find.

The Bear-Leaper does just that. Reaches his arm into the spittle. He pulls out the witch's copper pot. When he releases its treasury, a ball of smoke becomes the merman himself:

For the first few months in my tiny prison,
I swore reward for my saviour.
But no release, no release, no release.

As the next months passed,
I swore vengeance on the sea-wolf itself—
the ocean, and her fur of waves.
But no release, no release, no release.

Then finally, I swore death on whoever
would open my queasy chamber.
It would appear that three's the charm!

At this, Bear-Leaper produced the belt, and the merman speaks again:

Ah—that belt—might be
the trouble bringer. That's why this all started.
My head un-clouds with its sight.
I revoke my heavy chant—let us ally.

The merman takes his place on the rock, and scatters the waters with colour, the children grow fat with fish, greasy fingered with its roast, the old singing resumes between the sea, the woods, and the people.

But in the wintering time,
          a bear paws
                    the flaked ground
and the frozen roots of the forest.

The small eyes shine,
          alert to all that
                    peers in.

✳✳✳

The man startles, and wakes from the myth time. He glances around, and is pleased to see his daughter returned from the beach. The four women sit, enthralled and smiling in the cadence of Croc's telling. What eloquence he notes, so many different ways to tell a story, but Croc's language was especially fine, a high sound. He feels schooled, a little diminished in the best of ways. He looks over at his kiddo. Her hair is woven with a plait of autumn briars. She is quiet, but glows, as if the women have shown her some immense secret, out there on the beach.

He feels great loss, and big gratitude, all at the same time.

She sits at the ladies' table for a while, and then sidles over to Dad by the fire, ruffling the ears of a sleeping hound as she passes. She looks quizzical and amused.

"So...some men are secretly bears scratching at the doors of their girlfriends?"

"I think that's the size of it. You may want to keep an eye on that kind of thing, sweetheart. It appears we have herds of rhinos and furry little mice and old, precise arrangements with sea and land coursing through the lion's blood of our veins. Maybe we're only human for little bits of the day after all, or we need to think about what human means at all."

There's a sweet cooing from the table of the women. They glance over, and see that they have lit many candles. Little, stumpy yellow ones. They beckon the girl over, and bang on a beer glass with a Tatterhood spoon.

"A story for a story, dear Croc. From our newest and youngest visitor, a tale to fit her elegant jaw."

The girl-becoming-woman steps forward. Her voice is calm, but filled with jumps and electricity, leaps and pauses, utterly alive. The pub hushes around her.

✳✳✳

The Seal-Woman

One dusk, on return from a fruitless time on the sea, a fisherman on his way back to his croft spied the seal-people singing on the pebbly shore. As he crept past he found a sealskin lying over a shiny, wet rock. It smelt quite wonderful. Without thinking too much about it, he slung it over his shoulder and headed back to the cottage. Just as he got to the door, he heard a woman's voice behind him. As he turned, he saw it was a seal-woman, begging for her skin back.

In the man's life he'd never seen a woman like that before, he loved her utterly on sight. And love can make us reckless. He refused to return it, in fact took it into his croft and hid it in the chimney stack.

If you've ever lost your skin, you'll know that there's nowhere to go after such a catastrophe.

Over the years she bore him seven children, and grew to understand the love—straightforward as it was—that he offered.

There came a day he was at sea, and, as usual, the brine-scent of the waters caught her nostrils, and the far distant curvature of the grey waves haunted her little window. It made her breathless and restless and unhappy. She itched all over. Her children had seen this agitation many times. It was a haunting she carried. She thought she could even make out the shape of her old companions on the pebbly shore. They must have forgotten her after all these many years. There was silver in her hair now.

Kids know stuff. And her daughter slipped her hand into the little crevice of the chimney stack and brought out the skin. She'd spied her father, late at night as his wife slept, taking its scent to his own nose and breathing deeply. But you can't wear another's skin. That's a bad marriage.

The second she had her skin in her trembling hands she was gone.
She didn't cook for the children, didn't stack the washing, didn't leave a note, gone.

The children watched from the small window as she fled, the wind catching a cry from her which was not quite joy and not quite agony.

Soon, it was caught by the figures on the beach, a euphoric bellow coming from them. As one they turned and slipped into the bruise-coloured waves.

For the rest of his life, the husband would remember the request for her skin back.

Could there have been some other way?

For the rest of her life, the seal-woman would remember her children of the croft.

Could there have been some other way?

✳✳✳

And Croc muttered, looking into the bottom of his pint glass, "Is that not a love story?".

The man doesn't hear, he's up off his chair and cheering his kid.

the moon
the world
ASLEEP

Chapter Twelve

The Mood of the World in Sleep

A blue moon wakes the man. And he must do as his father did before him. He slips into his Levi's, shirt and boots, picks past his sleeping daughter and takes to the air. There is the luminous slosh of the shore waves, and the salt-perfume licking up and into his grateful nostrils. He sighs. And all around is slumber. In the fields and byres, in the hotels and guesthouses, in the boats where the fishermen doze in their nets for the early wake. And everywhere glows and murmurs with the moon's affections. The lobsters surge uncaught, jubilant for just a few hours more.

The Mood of the World in Sleep
The Mood of the World in Sleep
The Mood of the World in Sleep

Ah, but a full moon brings a fullness of feeling. He'd rather less, honestly. Less swell and surge, less sea-spittle, less loss, less sunken ships. He calls out to his god over the waves:

This weight is too much for me this weight is too much for me this weight is too much for me.

Alone, he cries again. Cries not even as he did as child. Deeper. Cries like he has every day for months and months. Till there are little daggers of watery sorrow creek-deep riven in his cheeks. He is frightened, frightened because some deep part of him does not want to live anymore. Some unmentionable dimension of his being does not want to get on top, or survive this experience. It is a terrifying and ungodly place to have reached.

There is one light that is not from the moon, but from around the doorframe of the nearby Kirk, up on the cliff. A hint of candle or lamp.

As he walks the white track to its door, he hears the ghost-sounds of the island: anvil bangs out the sword of a king, a corpse is found in the seaweed, a harp is struck as the snow flurries. The moon holds dominion over all dimensions of time, favouring none.

Inside the Kirk is a midnight priest.

There is a bannock of bread and a sip of ripe wine for the harrowed traveller. It is not good to look at the midnight priest directly but to keep your eyes almost unfocused, and let the flax of their language be the bridge. The rafters of this Christ-croft have masks of wolves, and owls and ravens in their timbers.

And this is what the priest told the washed up man. Of how the island came to be. Of how things can be born from what falls away.

✳✳✳

Cinderbiter

The blue churn, the green bridle; Scotland's jugged coasts. Near it there is a farm. The gull-shrill wind beats like medicine for a gummed ear. The family pinioned to the ground, praying to the seed-gods; the trance of field-work claiming all up to the silvered line of the shore.

All but one. Years before, the mother of the hut squatted out seven sons—sprouts, cubs suckling on the soured teat; sullen blonds wrapped dead-tight in the family inhibition. Six sons, dulled by necessity—butchered by weather. In the frosted dark, six sons line up with father to yoke themselves to earth-labour, to kiss the cold of Saturn's cross. Crook-backed, scoured like rounded loaves.

But the seventh sleeps by the fire's embers, so smeared by ash he seems more magpie than boy, locks hedgehog thick with ash; his mind, loosened by the flame's incanting. The boy is underground, adrift in the poet's dark roots of silence. Gilled, adept at the sea's pressures, crab-firm in the indigo black.

Stories come, squatting like lumps of coal darkly-bright in the Viking currents. The green teeth of the sea flower him with sagas, he befriends the banked moon. He is lifted, giddily over high desert: three years in the twigged circle of a condor. His slow heart sends a drum-thump through the tangled combustions of history. Rain-dancing through time, he is a god-torch, flickered on the cave wall, his haunch rich with prophetic ochre. And everywhere the snow falls.

Lazy, they say, watching his slow, tidal breathing. They who crack the earth, day in, day out. They who snake by in their gritty dedications. They whose hands know the rough licks of cattle, whose eyes know the hills pearled with rain. They whose arms are blue under the lambing snow. There is an egg of hate, fat amongst his wheat-yellow siblings, they long to string him up in the red barn; to hasten his passage through this life. They are a rough crowd for the bard. Every night, he stirs, becomes immense, looming in front of the land-blasted family. Myth telling. Stories lurch out beyond the ken of local knowledge. Sun on their backs, desert baked. Prophetic spurts come rapid from his travelled jaw. A mangling word-byre. Tundra snow and jaguar teeth spill onto the floor of the fire-flecked hut. He swears when his time comes he will rise with the hero-energy.

Father leans forwards with proud fists and scatters the grandeur. Says a serpent will lick the underside of the moon before that happens. All cackle, and relax gladly into the familiar atmosphere of hurt.

The ebony lump drifts off. There is always a killing to do round the farm. One night, guts of rain overturn on the farm. The darkness malignant, tough like a beetle's coat. Steel drops of water brace the farm's door. Amongst the commotion sounds a rough knocking; Something wants in. Father announces his coming to whatever waits. Dog barks; he coughs big and lively, and slouches to the shaking frame. It is the King's messenger. Cloak fat with water, royal brooch ornate, golden blazed amongst his costume.

He sits by the fire and accepts thin soup. He is large with news. There is a worm: the muckle-mester Stoor Worm, the serpent of Missgarrd, a horror coiled like a hateful rope around this world. The worm yawns and salt drifts of wave assault the bright corn. It breathes out and blonde hills become black feathers, ash piles, charred memory. Its vast head has moved north, its scaled mass is just a few miles off shore.

"We fear that great yawn, and the breath that will wrench us from the pap of life. Our King has called to the directions; hurled bones up at Orion's belt, gazed at his own hands' mysteries. Called on the spaeman, the northern magician who grins and says only killing will do: killing fire with fire.

First seven girls without bed-knowledge were found: bound tough, splayed crude to the rock—for the great head to extend its forked tongue and gather them into its inner-chambers. This darkness has occurred more than once until our people demanded some other way. The hamlets are empty of womb-maidens. So the spaeman went to the wilderness, was entranced, bog-crazy, rolled in thistle and gorse, got damaged by the forces and came back with worrisome knowledge: the death of this curse asks a high price. A flesh-treasure: the giving of the King's own daughter to the grey tongue of the worm. The King has announced by this fire that his daughter will marry any man soul-broad enough to take this serpent on; to roar with a bull's pride of its death. The wedding dowry will be the kingdom itself and the Old King's sword Sikkersnapper given him by Odin. My lord is the last of the

Old Kings, the last with a hand in that northern cosmos.

Thirty strong men were roused by that invitation; blood-gorged with the promise of gold. But at that beach they blanched, fell back, and wet the sand with their piss. My King has no faith in men like that. Now he takes his own sword from the chest behind the high table. Like a true champion he has brayed out that he will die in the foam rather than give his daughter to the worm. His boat is in a sheltered place tonight, tomorrow morning at dawn he will sail out, my King, dragging a sword too heavy for his years. So I travel the storm-line this night, farm to farm repeating the challenge to be great. To claim a sovereign's heft; to risk a sacrifice; to reach the beach by dawn and halt our King's suicide."

The rain-servant allows a murk of tears to mingle with his beard, and will not wipe the drops away. He rises, and returns to the shaking gale. He has many miles still to ride. The family slopes off to bed. That's more excitement than has landed on the farm in long years. Crescent-mooned in his charcoal nest, the boy hears mother and father, turning it around in their pillow talk, forgetful of the extra lugs sheltered in the gloom.

Mother wants to see the dawn reckoning. If all is doom, they may as well get to see the show. Father agrees, and reckons on Teetgong, their speediest horse getting them to the beach early. Mother raises herself onto one arm and asks just how is it that he gets such speed out of the horse? Like a mighty streak when aroused, a muscled blur over the gorse. Ah, men have secrets. He turns under the blanket, but she is insistent, offering all sorts of enticements. Her hands raise a hard sweat, and soon he is adrift in confession: "For Teetgong to stand I clap his left shoulder; to run, two claps on the right; but when I want the black gallop I bring out my fithfath: my cunning, my humours, my art, my sly magics. Now to make his hooves carve hot soil, I blow my thrapple, the windpipe of a goose my fetish blower that never leaves my secret pocket."

She chews on this knowledge and straddles him. Their cum-cries are muffled by their hands clamped rough on each other's mouths. Later, their hair mixed on the pillow, with the burr of the big man's snoring; and the boy crawls out of sight to his father's brown coat, piled by the bed. Inside is a pocket, hidden, where his hand finds the thrapple, smooth and somehow warm. This is the first of three great steals.

Out to the stables. The storming has passed. Now it is fierce clear, sharp as an Irish knife. Stars are ice-webbed on the blue curtain. The horse rears up and kicks, till the boy reaches out in the dark and pats Teetgong's left shoulder. He stills and submits to the bridle. As he pats the right shoulder, the horse surges forward and bellows.

Deep in himself, hawk-circling his well of memory, the father hears the neigh and wakes. Knowing that soul-din, that tender whinny, from the beast nursed since foal on the green hill, his heart directive, his appled-affection. His hand reaches into the black slit of his pocket. Gone.

The family scatters from their sleeping piles. Onto their beasts, half-dressed, stubbled like the field. Father leads, his guttural language drilling holes in the black air ahead of him. Rat a tat tat. He calls to his horse with all his slow wisdoms, claims back all his countless hours of care, for this hijack to cease, for his beast to come halt. Hi, hi, ho Teetgong wo! It almost works.

But away—the rider's blood cooks like red branches under his muck-skin, his tongue dirk-sharp with the urging. The horse tries to turn its head, desperate for the old calling, but the Cinderbiter turns the magic against its owner, and blows mad-hard on the thrapple. With that sound the horse becomes an occult arrow; flies beyond, far beyond the father and sons. He could have galloped off the very edge of the world.

On through the night: the son on the stolen horse, the father in the dark. How many fathers and sons, ride in the night like this? Father behind father behind father. Lonely like a Grendel.

Dawn is near as the boy reaches the beach. Saddle-bashed, he clambers off. Between the sea and the land is the thin strip of beach, and on that beach, a tiny croft. He slips inside. An old woman sleeps under a rough blanket, a cat at her feet. The hut groans woozily in and out as if it is she that breathes it. The fire in excitement all night, an iron pot beside it. As is his cinder-habit he gazes at the embers, then scoops a lump of peat from the fire, drops it quick in the pot and is off out with it. He does not see it open, the one bright eye of the crone. He does not see it open, the one green eye of the cat. They steadily watch: they have seen all this before. Their eyes close. This is the second of three great steals.

Air is chill, but dawn has come. Close to shore, the King's boat rocking on its anchor. A servant stands in the boat, so cold he beats his arms on his chest to warm himself. Cinderbiter shouts greeting and pretends to dig a firepit for a breakfast of limpets; then starts to yelp, and bellow—I see gold! A glitter-harvest right here before me on the beach. He squats in the half-light and starts to dig, whooping a treasure-chant to quicken the King's man. The servant is over the wave, heading ashore, dripping, then pushing the boy aside, snout in the dirt, paws churning as spades. Quickly into the harsh tide, the boy wades. The sun appears as a red ball over the land, and he lets anchor.

This is the third of three great steals.

Ahead is an island. But that is no island. The scaled-greasy-grey aquatic scalp of the serpent. End-bringer, Terror-wakener, Black worm. Seven yawns the creature makes, and then the tongue seeks flesh council, darting the waves. Our mottled dreamer aims the boat directly at it. Raging on shore, the King's men gather, but then are stilled staring at the loose-crow boy with a crone's pot on a stolen boat. They make crude bets for the swiftness of death's arrival.

On the third yawn, the betting gets hot: the boat and boy are sucked on the green brine slosh quick down the throat of the beast.

The Underworld, The Belly of the Whale, The Flesh Labyrinth. It was a phosphorescent world, lit up from the inside, with muscled tunnels, and surging, gurgling waters taking him deeper and deeper. Beyond chapel, holy books, tea leaves. Have you your adventure now, Cinderbiter? Is the dirt of the fields washed clean enough here for your poet's bones? He does not look left or right, but is an intended arrow and waits till the boat finally hits shallows. Into the glowing murk, he splashes. And takes his dagger—his muckle-ragger—from his belt. A sharp belly acid sloshes the walls; fierce stink drips but he picks his pace like an Indian runner in this subterranean luminosity, in this snake underground place.

The worm's liver he finds. The muckle-ragger cuts into it, deep, livid and bloody. Then from his swinging pail he plants the crone's ember in the splayed hole, the rupture. His dreaming-breath puffs wildly and the ember roars up again to flaming, charring, catching hold. When the whole liver is smoking, he splashes the tunnel back to his boat. The worm judders, wretches, starts to shape-lurch. He is getting cooked. The boat catches a stink of water from its belly, and carves up time and space in its exit from the serpent. Drenched in worm-foam, a black stick in the air—the boat soars and lands, hard and timber-blistered on the wet mud of the beach. The boy is flung clear. But the King and his men, the crone and her familiar, even his gathered family, are only half-looking at him. Because the world is changing.

The sky is a riot of black smoke from the worm's nostrils. Flood water from its gob loosens the waves. With a terror-smash it lifts its great head, its tongue shoots out and licks the underside of the moon, its whole body stands and tries to hold on, in tremor now. Above them all, the iron column of the beast goes mad-a-shake; from its slathering mouth, the teeth spray out. First tooth: the Orkneys. Second tooth: the Shetlands. Third tooth: the Faroes. Finally its body leaps back, far back, steaming into deeper waters. Coiled tight in a death-mass it passes. Iceland it becomes where the liver still smokes under burning mountains. Over time the people gather their senses back. Sky clears, the sun-gifted yellow beams. Some great energy has passed close by, but passed.

The King levels his gaze on the grimed-and-brined man. This drifter into the center of trouble, this magpie of the three steals. And places the heft of Sikkersnapper into that seer's calm hands. His family squints through the smoke, tiny-eyed. Then she comes:

Bright Daughter

Swan on the pool;
Hot moon, strong curved;
A roving deer under God's stars,
Full voice, voice that makes the beehives golden,
Dew lick the dark grass, fire-spark at the anvil.
Green cloak, brooch of fine white bronze
Grass does not bend under her foot.
She is her own country.
Full-thighed, flower arrayed.
She has budded slowly under the fur of snowy winter.
Read by the yellow candle, gathered sticks on the pagan hills,
Swum through a hundred acres of whale-thought.
She knows what stands behind her.

She is an Owl-Wife, knowledged;
No mere reward, but strong-minded; kestrel-swift, a stinging honey.
Our scare-crow man is agreeable to her, so different from those salted thugs of court.

There will be conversations for these
two, and bright rimmed goblets
and a walled garden with tall pines.

No Fear No Meanness No Evil

✳✳✳

The sermon is complete. The man wakes from the sing-song voice of the priest, and finds a bowl of herring and biscuit next to his arm. He places coins in the collection pot and walks back to his daughter, the blue night scarified with a dazzlement of cold white stars.

Chapter Thirteen

Becoming Crocodile

"We must have the stubbornness to accept our gladness in the ruthless furnace of the world. To make injustice the only measure of our attention is to praise the Devil."
Jack Gilbert

When he wakes the next morning, the girl is gone. There's a note:

Hey, Nutbucket.

The three silver ladies are taking me story-hunting again today. Be in the bar at eight o'clock sharp for the next instalment. We are walking into the middle of the island to find the story. We have to ask a stag who'll ask an owl who'll ask a salmon: what tale is just the right fit for my mouth?

Love,
you know who.

Meat! Meat! Meat!

That's a note to save. So he carefully folds it and puts it away in his pocket. They've had a room above the bar, and now he wanders downstairs to see about coffee, eggs even. No one knows anything about services in the middle of the night, or even the Kirk itself. At this point he's barely surprised.

Slightly disconcertingly, Croc is sitting exactly where he was last night. Has the beast slept? To his relief there's a genial fellow of the island serving up hot black liquid in chipped mugs from a huge tin of instant coffee. He notes three wet sets of footprints padding to the back door.

"The women? Did they have my kid with them?"

Tumnus smiles. "Yep, they came back out of the waters just now after their night swimming, full of beans and have whisked her off."

"Morning swimming, don't you mean?"

Tumnus begins, then stops himself, then begins again. "Do you remember last night's story? Sometimes a story is not a prophecy, or allegory, or set of rules, but an invitation. An invitation to figure something different out. Not all women have to abandon their families for the sea, not all men have to become lonely bears padding around the woods. There's ground for mediation, that's all I'm saying. A little bit of flexibility. So if I tell you the girls have been in their sea-shape all night, and have the boys on bar duty today, then it's a sign that even up here in the pagan north, so far from Piccadilly, we are maybe a little more evolved in how we work with the old stories." Tumnus smiles, "We figured some stuff out. Black and white's just not mythic. Now, would you like a nip of something in your coffee?".

The man declines and swings down into a chair by Croc, already chewing on the bitter black stuff. For a being that appears to have pulled some kind of all nighter, Croc is genial and welcoming, with plenty to say for such an early hour. "There you are, bright pulse. Not carrying quite so much of the world on your shoulders this morning?"

The man peers back, "I am not, it's true."

Croc asks, "How old are you?"

"Forty six."

Croc settles back, "Ah. There you have it. At almost any other time in culture you'd be about dead by now. Some part of you is in shock you're still here. That's the bit called mid-life crisis. It's an ancestral crack up deriving from the fact that you just may have been granted a second act that, deep down in the antelope dust of your bones you know is unique. These are years not necessarily writ large in your serpent brain. These years are virginal, new tracks out in the snow. The ancients are rubbing their heads on this one. It's called 'an evolutionary development', sugar-tits.

A man of your years may have seen a few things by now. Had his tree rattled a few times, lost some leaves. But what happened to you is something that still has the power, the choral catastrophics, the initiatory oomph to utterly derail you. Knocked off perch, the whole game. I'm talking about your conspicuous heartbreak understand?""

Man gently nods.

"If you really had a glimpse of the gods' reasonings for love—which they have for each and every one of us—you would most likely keep your head down, and not call time on a damn thing till your last breath. You are becoming crocodile."

Our man startles, "Pardon?"

Croc continues, "Becoming crocodile. There's a village I heard of, somewhere down in Africa, and at a certain point they take a man from the village out into the bush. They lie him down on the ground and for day after day they wallop his back with sharp sticks. Over time the skin on his back hardens into ridges like a flank of crocodile scales. If he lives through the experience they bring him back to his people and all know he can carry weight. He has learnt a little about suffering. He can be trusted in some fashion. One day may even become an elder. Would you bring your grief to someone who wasn't crocodile? Really? It'd be like bringing feathers to the wind.

And there's another village I heard of. That when a woman is giving birth in the hut, all the people, old and young, all the animals, all the birds, gather round the hut and wait. To them, when the baby cries it is asking:

Where am I? Am I safe? Do you claim me?

At that moment, the people, birds, animals, air itself roars its claiming of the young one, gathers her right in, makes absolutely stone-cold sure there's no possibility of a misunderstanding in that young soul that it's not loved, named and claimed.

Now, here's the hard stuff. The villagers believe if you don't receive such a thing within sixty seconds of being born, then you may spend the next sixty years trying to receive from one person the cry you should have received from the entire village on the moment of your birth.

That's too grievous a weight for any one set of shoulders to carry. But we've got millions now, grievous to their core, unclaimed, and thinking that love-cry is a mature sound. It's not. It's the sound a baby makes. That a baby is *supposed* to make.

I put you in that category my blossoming branch. So what are you going to do with your lot? Do you have capacity to walk through this world both heartsore but heart sober to the reality of this predicament? To stop blaming everyone but yourself?

If you love her, love her. There's not much that can be done about that. And grieve the bird that flew away. Let it be your walk in life. Have an elegant limp. There's a nutrition available in grief, an artfulness, but there's precious little in bitterness. And I felt a little of that on your tongue boy, across the waves.

There are implications to your suffering and hers and this story that may never be revealed to you. Worlds within worlds. So it is and always was. You are allowed to be wrecked, you are allowed to be blank, you are allowed to be empty. No one is a full moon all the time. Even the gods are filled with nuance, with shading, quiet gardens they walk in the cool of the day. Even the owl has her sadness.

You have to be ruined for a while. That's the realest, truest expression of the love that blew by one mid-summer's morning.

Now, did the girl take your grey-green stone?"

Man nods.

"Put your hand in your pocket. Can you feel something? Pull it out."

Man pulls out a small wine-red stone. It was not there last night.

"That's what you earnt. Your night wages. You can't say much in this world without it. Your signature will slide off the page. You gave innocence, but you got experience.

Now, stop holding it all together. Be deranged. Go walking on the beaches. You are so folded in you're practically a futon. Tell her what you need to say."

Our man of the raft is crying quietly. "She's not here Croc. She won't hear. I loved her I loved her I loved her."

Croc puts a big hand on his shoulder. "It's not she that has to, my petal. It's you. You're all tangled up on the barbed wire fence of love. Like a sad kite. This isolation you are in will become a black magic if you don't handle it deftly. Or badly. Or something.

But if you're going walking, take a story with you. Impolite not to have something to speak out as you go. I won't tell you why you need to hear it, only that you do. Your nets have great holes in them boy, dragging you down, only the riddles in the heart of these stories will mend them."

This time Croc's telling is quieter, more conversational, not dragging the whole bar in, but just our heart-wrung man. And so the net-mender begins.

**

Taligvak

It was a godless winter up in the north. So much snow you couldn't hunt and the people were starving. The hunters called in the shamans but nothing would work, no one could call the seals in. Death-hunger stood at the edge of the settlement.

Taligvak. The people thought of Taligvak.
The people didn't like Taligvak.

He lived on his own, in the most intense poverty. Edge man, no one would give him a daughter as a wife, and so he was without the warm clothes such a woman would create. His snow house was so small he slept sitting up, no stone lamps for heat, he was a blue being in the dark of his tiny home. People avoided him, but few doubted his power.

He had the odd magics that normal people do not have. With every deprivation, he had gained an ally. From the air, from darkness, he was surrounded. He had a spirit-entourage. They said there was nothing he could not accomplish, if he felt like it.

They grow so very hungry. They grow so very hungry. They gnaw on their skins.

The people sent three men to his slim dwelling to persuade him to use his magics. Two were so scared they dare not look inside, but the third made the request. He refused to leave his home in the snow. So they scuttled off and a woman soon presented Taligvak with boots and cosy mittens. He made his way to where the people were gathered. Though he called through the entrance, when he came to the folks he stopped at the door, refusing to go further. He just stood, looking, mute and frightening.

One of the people called out:

"We will give you warm skins, mittens, clothes—you can live with us in the warm. Only make a hole right here at the igloo's edge and bring the seal to us. Otherwise we all die."

He stood still a long time. Then he slipped into the dwelling by the side of the ice wall and commanded them to dance, and to not look at what he was doing. Not ever to look.

As the people whirled and sang, he simply blew on the ice, every time he did so, a little hollow appeared. It took a long time. Finally there was a bubble of water and he let the dancers see. Then he made them turn away again and dance.

He held a tiny harpoon in his hand, tiny, ridiculous. He held it up over his head and began to pray:

Oh a chubby one comes
From the deep blue black
Much fat on the animal much fat
What happiness when it is
Pulled from the bottom of the world
And laid out on the floor of the igloo

Even while he was singing, a seal came that he harpooned. It was dragged by the people to a lean-to, where he told them to remove the head of the harpoon and return to him. Then the meat was cut up, and the people fed. As they ate, he sat and stared into the hole, forbidding all to watch.

Happiness comes
When a fat seal wallops
Onto the ice
My harpoon is a magic snare
That hauls them in

Even while he was singing, a seal came that he harpooned. And this continued, the crooning over the hole, this meat for the people. And they survived the winter.

From that time on, Taligvak was respected and given what he needed, but tended to remain a little apart. But when the people travelled inland, he came with them a little behind, with his skins, his knife, his sewing needles—needles they say cut from the bones of a rabbit foot.

When the thaw came the people camped near Padleq river, a little distance.

Taligvak was alone again and he saw everything.

He saw the spring come
And the caribou saunter
To the rivers that had
Once been streams
He saw snow become
Brown earth
He consumed all experience

He collected beached wood, gathered his snares and some rabbits that he had cleaned and stripped of skin. He was agile with his knife and whittled the wood into a frame then stretched the skins, once they had been soaked. He snared a loon and cut its neck in a circle to make straps, with which he used to sew his skins together.

As he worked, he saw a flank of caribou across the water and knew fear. But he gathered himself, and with just his knife he walked towards one and took its life. As well as the meat he took the shinbone and split it lengthwise by hammering it on a stone. Half of the bone he mounted on wood to make a spear, with which to hunt more caribou. To take them down with their own bone. With this, many caribou were killed, and nothing was wasted. The economy of his mind fashioned a use for everything.

He soon saw people coming towards his little structure of stones and earth, and saw that it was the people from before, and that they were starving. They had come for the plentiful fish of the river, and a little bit of curiosity to see if he was still alive.

He placed a scrap of seal skin on the floor, something the people had rejected long ago as not worthy. On it he placed a few tongues, a dump of marrow, a little bit of meat. This was a big hungry group, and this was clearly not enough grub. Their eyes were narrow.

He told them to look away and started to sing:

Look who has arrived at Taligvak's place
How lucky I have tongues to offer
And that fatty caribou
You know all about that
I don't need to tell you!
And this weedy plate
This paltry plate

Is groaning with meat

A few dared a glimpse, and saw the scrap of seal skin piling up with meat.

They have come from
The banks of Padleq river
To my digs
And I took down
A fatty caribou
With my thin strapped kayak
You know all about that
I don't need to tell you!
Now look at this plate
This weedy plate
This paltry plate
Is overflowing!

The people ate and ate and still could not consume the meat on Taligvak's magic plate.

Blue man
In the darkness
Sleeping upright
Seeing everything

✳✳✳

The man finishes his coffee quietly, and heads out. That strange story starts to work his bones. He can't hold onto it, it's like a salmon in hand, but it's something. Maybe it's something to do with the relationship between loneliness and magic. Yes, maybe it's that. That unpalatable negotiation for insight. He can't tell. But it chews, chews, chews away—the paltry plate is overflowing.

At eight o'clock on the nose he is waiting for his kid. The people of the pub gather a few candles and poke the fire. She comes in with the women, a little shy glance at Dad but radiant.

As if she's found the source of something, as if she's grown wings. He loves that he knows nothing of what is transpiring with the women, only that it's the real dram. She begins her second telling.

Come muse! Start where you may,
And speak to us of our time too.

✳✳✳

A Drum Used For Magic

There was an old couple, up in the north, who wished to marry off their daughter. There was a steady procession of suitors but she cared for none of them. One day two brothers came, no more interesting than the rest it seemed, but a strange thing happened. Her cheek flushed in their presence.

As they went to leave she walked with them to the door of the igloo. Once there they put back on the skins they had left outside. On and on they went, until they were no longer men putting on skins, they were white bears. Two magnificent white bears.

They stole her away, they stole her away, they stole her away.

They came to a hole in the great white ice and dived in. Into the terrible cold and into the darkness went the girl, all she could make out was the vast shapes of the two white bears. And down in the deep waters they came to another hole that she could not enter. The bears disappeared into it and she was alone.

It was darker on one side of her than the other, she presumed the darkness was north, so she headed south, towards what little brightness she could discern. Her feet had touched the bottom of the sea now, so she walked. But as she walked, creatures of the deep altitude started to nibble and bite at her body. Bit by bit, mile by mile, they stripped her bones. By the time she came to the light, she was just bone and mind.

She swam upwards and found herself back above the ice. Even as a woman of bones, she needed to eat, she needed shelter. She constructed a simple igloo, and a little platform for meat. But she needed furs, she needed warmth. Some distance away she saw a big igloo, and found a caribou nearby, freshly killed. She stole it away, dried the hide to sleep under, and ferreted the meat on her platform.

From that time on, if she dreamt about something, she received it the next day. But no matter how much she ate, her skin didn't grow back, she was a woman of bones.

One day she saw the hunters from the igloo about to hunt seal, and started to walk towards them. They had never seen anything like her and fled, terrified. That night, they told their old father, who no longer hunted, what they'd seen.

"Well, I'm nearly dead, nearly an ancestor. I will go see her."

The next day the old man went to her igloo and found the woman of bones by the entrance. They looked at each other for a long time and she then invited him in. Inside it was very bright, very light from the stone lamps. They ate and then fell asleep as the great blackness came. All night the heavens circled them.

In the morning she asked the old hunter who could no longer hunt to make her a drum, a tiny drum. He set to work, stretching skin and sinew until it was ready. She took all light from her bright igloo and began to drum and to dance. She spoke the same ancient words, over and over.

The tiny drum is growing
The drum used for magic
The tiny drum is growing

When the stone lamps were relit there was a woman of flesh as well as bone. She was back in the origination of her shape. They were both delighted by the development. Soon she blew out the lamps and drummed and danced and sang again. When she relit the lamps, the old man was young again, flushed with vitality, back erect, eyes flashing.

When the hunters returned to their igloo, they did not recognise the young and happy pair walking across the snow towards them. But as the lamps were lit, and the story told, soon they would understand.

And this is how the girl who did not wish to marry found her husband.

***

So there they sit in the bar, time as still as could be. Fanboy and the storyteller. The young woman is leaning back a little, gleefully, and one of the women has plonked a rather fetching Trilby on her head. Dad's full of questions:

Why does she need an old man to help make her flesh?

With this last question, the girl leans forward and grins. "Because life's a contact sport Dad. And you can't do everything yourself. I don't need a Hercules complex thank you very much. AND in an old story, maybe there's a little bit of you in all the characters. Lots of bits having conversations with other bits. That's MY old hunter that's helping ME out."

(At this she tugs on his beard. Not recommended unless you are his daughter.)

Relieved the stories are over, and flushed with their success, she continues, "The silver women are teaching me stuff. And they've got me working with my hands too."

He asks, "Weaving, knitting?"

"Sword fighting. They say finding a voice in this world isn't easy. Specially if you're a girl. They like this quest to Greece we're on, but to get all the way we've got be tough sometimes. Face fears. And my fears may not be yours. Cause you're my dad. They are saying things to me in a way you can't.

I've always heard you tell stories but this is different. They have surprises when they pop out of me. They land differently. They get to say what they need to say without telling everybody my address and shoe size. I'd like to keep it that way.

But I get anxious y'know. Small stuff as well as big. This is a lot of beauty to push out of my mouth when I may be feeling pretty crap inside. And the silver ladies say there's a lot hidden away to help me in fairy tales, 'the true history of the world' says the poets, so the *Goose Girl* is as important as *War and Peace*.

Man and girl hug.

Dad shakes his head with admiration, "It's amazing that you call out for what you love. What you stand for. God almighty, here you are. Beauty-making, not just digging for victory. Though I wouldn't complain at its arrival. And y'know, as we get older a little appreciation of what hell can look like arrives, and the fact that almost all real initiatory work is to bear it. To bear the unbearable. I mean really, that's what much of it's about. That's where most of these elaborate, initiation rituals and three-day stories come from.

And feeling crap?

Down in the Greek underworld, a character called Ixion turns forever around on a grinding wheel, punished for having an eye for Hera. What dread or anxiety churns us on its underground wheel? Now, not you or me is free of Ixion's wheel, but just naming the being, and recognising it is awfully useful.

And to know that the wheel slows to a halt in the face of the luminous music of Orpheus. All monsters like a present. Especially when it carries their scent. So the next time that anxiety kicks in, remember who's down in your belly, and what they may need to be courted by. Remember that you're still in the story. Take down a musical instrument says the poets.

When fear and anxiety sweep in, we risk them cutting the cords to our soulful waters, and the restorative goddess—Sedna—that lives there. Remember Sedna? I know you do. The monsters cause us to lose hope. A huge victory for them is when you no longer look to your own nourishment. We look around and nothing is growing, the sky is bleak even if horribly blue, the animals no longer move to the yellow moon of our heart. Do you remember C. S. Lewis? In his language this is the place of the Snow Queen and the freezing of all the animals. It's deadly there, be very careful. And maybe when we fight we can carry Sedna's anger as an energy with us.

Geez kid, as you well know, life is not talking-circles and Kombucha most of the time. It's slippery, nuts and confusing, with any confirming story occurring only over the passage of time. Heart education also involves protection of the heart, especially when under attack. No soft white underbelly when the crows are circling. You need the tuition of Scathach. Your Silver Women will know all about her.

Russians call it Katabasis: a juddering descent from comfort and certainty. You know it's arrived because it feels absolutely fucking horrible. Excuse my French. Underworld. Big hero moves usually have to be replaced by a whole other form of education. Baba Yaga is terrifyingly present, with her pale skulls and demanding staggeringly quick decisions. Baba is worth proper study.

Sometimes you have to break free from the hunter's snare, fighting tooth and bloodied claw, losing feathers, shake the world-tree to call down the gods for your protection. Betrayal, entrapment, divorce, harassment, deranged neighbours; take your pick of battlefield."

The girl interrupts, "Divorce? Dad, I'm twelve. But I see where you're going."

He continues, "When Cu Chulainn, the warrior of Ireland needed every shred of sentimentality scrubbed from his body he was taken into the apprenticeship of this Scathach I mentioned—*The Shadow*—the trainer of warfare and its skills. She taught the ability to pole-vault over your enemies' attacks, also to be able to fight under water, and under extreme pressure.

So to be in the presence of Scathach is to forget the steady middle road but understand both the leap and the dive in combat; to make an ally of air and water. Wherever they aim their blow, you simply aren't there.

Her example is this: don't stand directly in the way of big hits, anticipate them and develop strategy. All good warriors have great capacity to see at the edge of their vision, genius lives on the margins. Side-step, full-attack when required, play-dead when you have to, and do not, do not give up.

And another thing, at a moment like that: now is not the time for your tears.

You may remember the old Russian firebird story when a weeping hunter unburdens to his horse and his horse claims, 'Don't weep now. The trouble is before you'. This is a way of counselling the right time and place for the Keeners. Keening is a kind of grief singing.

After a battle there are the Keeners: the ones who let the sorrowful cry of the death-space lift up and over the fight. Myth tells us we are many; and when we have to fight, that is not the time to let our own keeners claim dominion. That is not the moment to let the sword wobble with the deep feeling they invoke. Be accurate, sober and without mercy. If you fluff the blow, the monster jumps up again.

When you have to go to war, there are others that can carry the keening for a while, or cleanse your weapons in milk afterwards, will take you in whatever shape you return from the combat in. You will always be beautiful to us. We should try not to make excuses, or fib, or obscure, but be humbly grand in just the perfectly imperfect shape we are.

You've heard me tell the Invasion stories of Ireland, can you remember that? This poem comes from that tale. This kind of thing is called, *Knowing What Stands Beside You*. I think I've got it memorised:

When the Big-Father of Ireland
had finished his hour of love
with the daughter of his enemy,
she rose before him:
Whatever crossroads you
come to, I will be standing there.

Whatever river curls your feet,
I will be standing there.
There are a hundred roads
to the battle that will kill you,
and I will block every one of them.
Each move of her tongue
over the ivory palace of her teeth
bound their lives to the Otherworld.

Even driving the kids to school today,
I remembered that promise.
And we wander this world deranged
for its absence, drunk in the Russian trenches."

She looks at her old man for a moment agape, "I can't believe you got to squeeze in a mention of the school run."

Chapter Fourteen

What Mayaki Heard at the Smokehole

The bar is filled with boozy chatter now. It's so warm a window is open letting in chill night air as the fire slow roasts the hut of dreamers. We can see the two travellers waving their arms about, and the kid attempting to sip his stout as Dad bangs on and on. As they peer through the smoke—the ban has not quite reached this island—she spots the oldest silver haired lady gesturing to her, she seems to be mouthing, "One more! More one!"

At this, the woman makes her way through the tables groaning with ale and bowls of herring, and beckons to Croc. For the first time since they have arrived at the tavern, he rises from his seat and makes his way to her side, and what has been functioning as a kind of storyteller's corner.

An excitement fills the room, as if folks know they are about to see something rare, or a rumour twisting into a straight out occurrence.

"One more, one more story for tonight. To give our visitors strength. Courage. For tomorrow they will leave for the final part of their journey. To warm, green waters. To our Lady of the Southern Isles. A story passed into our ears here from the Chukchi of Siberia.

Long ago, a Russian ship made its way to our harbour, and this immortal tale was whispered over dark beer by its tribal crew into this very room. A story that is a nomad itself, designed to travel. Dear Croc, I believe you and I were both here on that very night. Would you tell it with me. Shall we weave our lives into the telling one more time?"

Croc finally looks fully at the woman, with a look of long-earned admiration on his face, and for once a gradation of tenderness enters his voice. "I do believe it would be an honour."

As they begin, the northern lights turn and twist green and purple in a rapturous night sky, and birchbark canoes pull quietly into the northern bay. Old friends returning.

A drum bangs and sparks its ancient patternings through the words.

✳✳✳

What Mayaki Heard at the Smokehole

Out on the Taiga there was a bad man with two wives, his name being Canda. The women were called Gayula and his favourite, Ayaula. How he adored Ayaula. Ayaula's only labour was to daily comb her husband's hair, so it glistened sleek and magnificent in the firelight. But for Gayula it was different; she lived in a ramshackle hut some distance away, with a grinding litany of tasks—cooking, sewing, feeding the ravenous dogs that howled all day and night.

Over time, Ayaula had a baby girl, Gandusa, whilst Gayula bore a son, Mayaki. The two kids had utterly different temperaments, Gandusa was sullen and tent bound, whilst Mayaki was a voracious hunter, and always eager to assist his mother with her endless chores. You would see him slipping through the white larch out in the bright morning with his bow, always bringing something back for the pot.

One day in play, Mayaki accidentally sent his sister flying to the ground. In a rage, Canda roared onto the scene and berated his wife for teaching the boy to be an aggressive lout. Ayaula set about Gayula with her staff and wrestled her to the dirt. Once down, Canda grabbed a deadly sharp, forked twig and skewered Gayula's eyes out, one after the other. "These are the eyes with which you should have watched over our daughter," he bellowed, then hurled her eyes into the cold stream.

From then on Mayaki loyally attended to his mother, feeding her, washing her, combing her hair. His childhood, such as had been, was over. Time passed and he grew to a young man. One day, Gandusa came tripping through the forest to spy on the poor relatives. Mayaki bellowed at her, and she turned tail to run to her father and report a new drama. Oh, Mayaki hurled rocks, fired arrows, used his fists, all nonsense.

But Mayaki had the old magic on him, the magic that normal people do not have.

He tapped his head with a special stick and became a bird.

I had feet —now claws
I had mouth—now beak
I am a feathered terror coming
I can hear everything
I can see everything

He flew to his father's tent and listened in at the yellowed smokehole at the arising gossip, resting on a crossbeam. Gandusa burst into the tent, claiming she had been set upon by her brother, a terrible and protracted beating, saying how arrogant he was. Her father erupted from his furs, claiming:

"If Mayaki is as powerful as you suggest why doesn't he find his mother's eyes, search for her vision? If he pulls that off then his boasts will have more weight."

That was enough information. He knew what to do.

With his blind mother they constructed a birch-bark canoe, and he set out to find his mother's eyes. She had tried to dissuade him, saying he was too young, that she could live without them, but he wasn't having it.

I give myself to the sea
like I gave myself to Taiga
I bob and surge on my canoe
through all assessments of reality

For many days he travelled. He came to a far shore and two girls playing with a pair of black eyes, throwing them back and forth across a fire.

He joined in the game, all happy and playful, but with his heart pummelling in his young chest. "We found these squidgy black stones on the shore, washed up," they intoned. Back and forth it went until he finally got both into his hands. In a second they were in his leather pouch and he high tailed it across the pebbles to the green waves and birch bark canoe. Though they wailed from the sea's edge, they could not catch him.

On his return he lit the fire, made some stew, and sat his mother very still. He placed the stones into her sockets. She blinked. She saw the whole world. Her vision was returned.

And for a time all was well, until little Gandusa came tripping through the forest. She saw that Gayula could see perfectly well and ran back to her father, relaying the development. As a bird, Mayaki followed, sheltering on the yellowed smokehole.

"If he really was that substantial, he would marry the girl from beyond the seven hills, and pay the bride-price of seven matching fox tails without hesitancy. No man has accomplished it."

He knew what to do.

In one day he had traversed the seven hills and come to the settlement of the old blind man, Mafass. He lived with his wife and their raven-tressed daughter, Biala. Her face was pale and round, and she wore a dress intricately constructed by her own hand. Both of these young ones felt their backs straighten, and their pupils grow large and dark with longing as they peered shyly at each other.

Baila spoke: "You must cross another seven hills and seven rivers till you come to the fox trail. Stand to the side and keep quiet until you spot the fox with eight tails. Now hurry, because they only come by once a day, at noon."

She gave him a patchwork cloak of her making, and just as potent, a glance of love.

He traversed, sloshed, scampered and wheezed his ways across the hills, fording the icy streams till he got to the place of the fox trail.

He disguised himself as a tree stump to the wonderment of the foxes:

We have been this way before
And no tree stump
We have witnessed stream
And gully, squirrel and sable
But no tree stump

When the eight-tailed fox sauntered past, with his thick and fiery brushes on full display, he too wondered at the new tree stump. He halted. It was not there yesterday. As he gazed, engrossed, Mayaki lurched forward and in one agile stroke, with his blade took seven of the brushes of the fox. Tucking them into his belt he brought them back as bride-price for Biala. She was delighted with the outcome, and returned to be his wife, with his black-eyed mother.

And for a time, all was well, until Gandusa came tripping through the forest. She saw the beautiful woman and described her in detail to her slobbering father, who flushed with lust for this wife of his son. Up by the smokehole, his son heard his rant:

"If he really was fit for such a woman, he would waste no time in demonstrating his power: by crossing seven hills and seven terrible swamps where he would come to a tree. No feeble thing, but a tree with scales of a serpent, with leaves of gold and silver, and whose falling blossom rings out as loud and as clear as a struck bell.

A man of substance would uproot such a tree and bring it back to our tent for the whole family to admire."

With that he scratched his crotch, settled back in the furs, and commenced to fantasising about his daughter in law.

Mayaki knew what to do.

He took himself across seven hills—huff and puff—and through ghoulish swamp till he came to its centre where he beheld the tree predicted by his dark father. It started to snow, flake over flake from grey yellow sky, tumbling endlessly down. But, undaunted, he gripped the trunk of the scaled tree and started to tug it from the frozen mud.

Finally, he whirled it above his head and commanded it to fly to his mother's straw hut and take root. He hurled it with all he had, and a little bit more he didn't know he had.

It passed through quadrants of time and disorder, calm and eternity, till it landed thump and deep in the earth by his mother's flimsy hut, sparks crackling and shrieking from the dirt as it did so.

On his return he warned Biala and Gayula a terrible storm was coming, the like of which they had never seen before. They sealed up the hut. And the storm came with a meanness, a malice, a straight up bad feeling that demolished everything in its path, flattened stands of birch and larch, levelled the steep little gullies of the Taiga. But in the threadbare hut, the three were snug by the fire under skins, and dreamt deep.

In the morning, Mayaki's father and his other wife and his sister had completely disappeared, even the tent. Vanished. Only one ember glinted in the fire pit as evidence they ever existed. I cannot tell you that their absence was mourned.

But in this new world, at the shimmering navel of it creation, the serpent tree continues to thrive, Biala continues to create beauty from her needle, Mayaki to hunt, and the dark-eyed mother to enjoy her years by the life-giving fire. To this day grows a tiny poplar and a silver birch tree by their hut.

✳✳✳

The story is complete now. All the way through the two voices carry it, one tailing off, one picking up, melodious and gruff and sweet, a hundred unspoken stories hanging off its wingtips. By now the autumn sky is ablaze with the marvellous, and everyone carries their pints and drams outside. These eternal islands, these waterways to the deep north are a kind of heaven tonight. Dad rocks quietly back and forth with wonder, with the kid's hand in his pocket.

PART FOUR

KIND

OR

SAVAGE?

Chapter Fifteen

The Door of Mercy is Still Open

They awake to an island in the making: the banging of rivets from the blacksmith, dunes covered in blond splinters of timber. Pots of tar bubble, dogs bark, axes strike, and runic script is smudged by strong thumbs onto a spine of ribs being crafted—it would appear their humble raft is getting a makeover. Shark, herring, sardine and cod is salted and handed in, bannocks of bread as yellow as the moon.

There is singing, low and focused as they work. The man and his daughter stare down from their window for a moment, dumbstruck. Then they are scrambling into their coats and hoofing it out onto the beach. The islanders are typically modest, sweet even. They just see it as being part of the old voyaging traditions of their place. You help out.

The three silver ladies are speaking in a sing-song way:

The winds will treat you different now
South South South

Our spaemen—our magicians and hedgerow women
Have negotiated a clean road across the whale's foamy back
In days you will be at the temple of our lady of the south

Find that temple: repair it, clean it, make the libations she requires,
Light the fires, sweep the floor, smoke the herbs

We will swim alongside here and there
Until you leave our quadrant of the marvellous

To Crete sail, and you will find what you are looking for
A story, as stories have been your secret sail-wind this whole time
You will come to many islands:

Ignore Circe's, Calypso, Aeolus King of the Wind, Polyphemus's,
Hold your nerve till dear Crete.
And you will hear what you need to hear
From the being you need to hear it from.

There are hugs from Croc, Tumnus and the others, and the women just slip under the waves. And are seals again. The raft—robust, magicked now—slips from shingle to brine and then they are away again.

The girl sits at the front now, laughing and waving at the seal women. She's like the prow of the beast pointing and shouting, "Dad! Southward ho!"

✳✳✳

"La vie profonde attend"

"Deux cidres s'il vous plaît"

And on the deck the man—belatedly some would say—is trying to teach himself French. The old sounds in his jaw just don't fit. They don't.

Today the sky is sharp-teethed blue, and everything is alive:

Sing cuckóu, nou! Sing cuckóu!
Sing cuckóu! Sing cuckóu nou!
Loudë sing, cuckóu!

And why French he wonders even to himself? Surely Greek. Nope. He again is in his remembering. Maybe on a different face of love to the one he splashed into the Dart for.

Three years before he sat by the bedside of a dear friend in the last hours of her young life. A French woman. He said and sang very old things to her. Later, her husband and her father and her brother and him carried her tiny, elegant bird-body down the stairs, every doorway a station as they processed to the small room that for seven days would carry her body in wake. Her beloved women came and clothed her in her very finest dress, combed through her black and silvery hair with deep red flowers.

Very early the next morning, a group of them, like a cadre of lions led by her husband, ran—ran—several miles across open fields to an old workshop where a heavy oak casket was then crafted; built by the men of the town that loved her. He'd sat with others by lantern at night, and told her stories, would bear witness to her man's delicious grief music, and on the morning of the funeral, he and their two little girls heated beeswax in a small pan, sang—*good where we've been, good where we're going to*—and sealed up the coffin on their incredible mother and his wife with something sweet and warm. And, as they would say, it wasn't nearly enough. Their courting of her departure will last for years and years.

So what did it mean to stay the course for a family that have endured such a thing?

It looked like fidelity to goodness. Not niceness, but goodness. Love like a lion's beating heart. The kind of thing that's just not meant to be allowed anymore. It means in its terrible whittling away an incredible essence is revealed. An essence that changes the way you live. From them, their friends and radiating outwards.

It looked like fidelity, under the most extreme of experience, to the core emanation of beauty and kindness in the face of the terrible mysteries of existence. As far as he can fathom, there is simply no other way to behave.

Anything else is too deathly-sophisticated, or existential, just plain jaded. Anything else claims total victory for fear and none for the deepening of the soul.

So, on his raft, on this blue and earned day, this is what he knows:

That if you are lucky enough to have the opportunity to reflect at the end of a life, then love is revealed as the great currency. It's the thing. The treasury. It's what mattered. Few gloat on a business success, or property portfolio at that point, how they royally screwed someone over.

How well did I love? Who did I love? And how was love central to the life that I made for myself? And some don't like the insight of the moment.

When the lots are counted, when we are gathered in, we will find that it was love that counted. Love expressed, given, received, fought for. To believe in the full life that is your bequeathed inheritance, not the subterranean half-life that terror and impoverished minded bullies will try and spike your wine with. You are too good for that. Remember Rilke: "wherever I am folded there I am a lie".

Most of the things that have grown to true stature, longevity and surety of beauty in his own life have come from incredibly testing and frightening periods. This isn't fetishising disaster, just a statement of fact.

There are times when he's had to lie low, play possum, as slander shuddered the air. No big statements, no grand gestures, just keeping his head as close to the ground as possible as the bullets whizzed by. Six months on the ice flow. A year in a hollow tree. But, like magnets and iron, that longing for the full life always returns. And step by step, it emerges to its succulent fullness. The price of not following it is far, far too high.

Run towards it. There is still time. The door of mercy is still open.

✳✳✳

Swish Swish Swish

And you should know, that along the way, the raft started to fill up.

On the boar jut of the Welsh coast a cormorant joined them, and a young man released early from prison was waiting with his satchel by the door, and old Yevgeny, and all the emigres and gypsies from the boat—even hauling their black and white TV onto the raft, and not forgetting, of course, furry beings we barely have the name for anymore.

And then further into the miraculous: a girl with a tattered hood, and a queen with a red flower on her breast, an owl with the eyes of a woman, and on and on into the night. An enormous, dignified hairy man who sops moisture at the back, refusing all towels, a skillful young Rom who plays the fiddle, a fox woman who leapt straight from a mountainside and onto the boat, and is surrounded by laughter and things to chew on.

On this boat no one is refused, mocked or made small. Unless you want us to praise the inventive splendour of being small. Which is a different kind of vast.

This is a raft alive with stories, stories that celebrate reunion with all the others, so different in shape but so united in life force, in the grief and wonder of it all so gloriously threaded. And so they sit and laugh and weep and gossip as it crafts its way south.

The urging currents lead them out of our time altogether
Though in the dark the shipping forecast still crackles
From a radio. Some delicate thread between worlds.

They pass Milk Wood and Dylan Thomas carousing on
The sea-shanty, sea-scarlet, sea-shore, sea-shore
His stout in one piggy hand, his double tot in the other,
They catch the scent of Dai Bread's bakery, and hear
The troubled dreams of Captain Cat, as his lost boys

Eternally call to him over the purplish churn: Dancing Williams,
Jonah Jarvis, Curly Bevan, Alfred Pomeroy Jones, as,
In his roaming dreams, he dishes out rum and lava bread
And forms his difficult repentance.

Oh Dylan, laughing priest of the lanes of Ceredigion

To Eleanor of Aquitaine
And a changing poetic world
No hawk of the well
But nightingale of the pine

Far distant castles
And lovers' intrigues
Minstrels in the gallery
And early morning rides
Past mossy towers
As women glow
Like cuticles of the moon
From the pentangles
Of their private windows

As horses' bridles
Jingle jangle jaunty like
And Isolde gallops
Over the midnight drawbridge
As the whole pagan world
Cheers her on

And on and on

Past Lorca
In the orange groves of the Alhambra
Where he strolls with his leopards
In the dawn light
Preparing for a sword fight
As the bells call for mass
As widows walk
Dewy grasses to whisper
To a handsome priest

And the raft passes Gibraltar
Where for a little while
In another century
The man's mother was briefly raised
And Barbary apes flipped and flopped
On hot rocks and Helios
Beat down his hot patterning
On that azure gateway to Africa

As they pass the strait
He hurls coins in the green delirious sea
For Alec, Christine, Jenny and Sarah
He can see them walking the harbour together
Always in that moment, 1956, their whole
Life ahead of them

And in the back of the raft,
The shipping forecast
Still crackles

The raft has curved eastwards now, eager into
Mediterranean waters

And the man hides the names of the woman he loves
In the curvaceousness of his language

Heart-wrenched and sleekly sorrowed
He may be, but
His love for her is the raft itself.

To the quadrant of the Olympians they are coming: and the cave nymphs,
And centaurs and living fuses of dappled fire that bring the streams and rivers
And oceans to their fullness. Past the Libyan sea, Ionian sea, Sicilian sea, and
Towards the Cyrenic sea, past Corsica and Sardinia, past Numidia and Libya.

And under the blue tent of the sky: where the goddess Eurynome created the seven
Planetary powers and a Titaness and a Titan to watch over them: for the sun,
Theia and Hyperion, Phoebe and Atlas the yellow breasted moon; for Mars come
Dione and Crius, for Mercury Metis and Coeus, Jupiter, Themis and Eurymedon,
For Venus come Tethys and Oceanus, and Rhea and Cronus for the brooder Saturn.

Oh Poseidon, salt-maned terror of the waves,
Whopping great shit-kicker of the terrible deep
Please have mercy on our few, salty twigs

Oh Helios, blond coin of the heavens, noble chariot to all that grows
Please have mercy with the rage of your rays

And they came to an island.

Up onto the shingle as gently as bee lands on flower.

And old Yevgeny, from the back of the boat called:

"Will these people be kind or savage?"

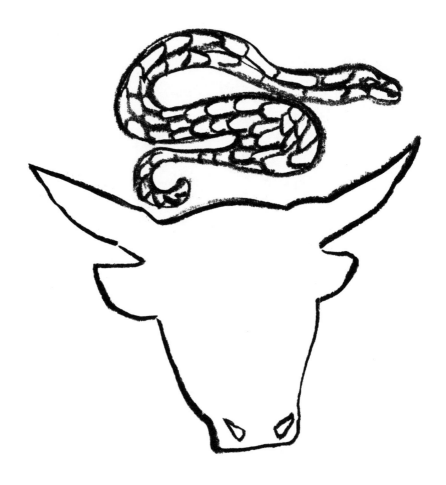

Chapter Sixteen

Cista Mystica

The island is a basket, and not just any basket, it is a Cista Mystica: the woven casket that the followers of Dionysus carried into their deepest ceremonies. Within the casket is fresh rushes, and lain on the rushes is a serpent, a snake, the living god itself. Not a representation of, but at that moment *is* the Lord of the Vines himself: *The Loosener, The Deep Drinker, Night Light, Bearer of All Moisture, Anax Agreus—The Hunter.* To have arrived at this island is to have arrived at the House of the Mysteries, the inner lamp in the centre of all tumult, the ember in the heart of all ruin.

Flood of grape and dingly dells abound. Leopards prowl by the waterfall, and shady pools hold shoals of fast moving fish. Streams glitter-gurgle and warming lashes of sunlight crash down through the emerald bough. It is hard to remember ever having been anywhere but here, it pushes all memory aside, at least for a little while. They have come through the eye of the needle, rowdily agape in the reeded centre of the heart's wine.

The small island is surrounded by a crest of trees, its encasement; rushes and vines its tangling floor, bowls of incense spume their fragrance over the salt-stiff arrivals. In times such as these, the place to find Aphrodite is in the centre of the treasure casket.

Waiting for them is an immense bull, with a snake wrapped loosely around its vast belly and shoulders, garlands of flowers around his neck. The travellers have grief-walked themselves into the dazzle-dark of this lair of holy lairs. No map, no franchise, no ambition-strewn logic could have delivered them here. Only the lonesome creel of their heart-entanglements.

Little old women in Harlem apartments get here, long widowed Dubliners get here, the child torn hawk-swift from their childhood gets here. The Cista Mystica is a second from your elbow, not even that, and absolutely nowhere on any map you can name. The realest of the real.

The bull and the serpent speak as one—the strangest sound. All sink to their knees.

You are almost there. Almost. But not tonight.

You will get the bends if you take one pace
Further in. The bounty ahead will outpace
Your mind so utterly you will be ravaged
By their truth. So cool your boots.

Your guardian in these shuddering dimensions
Is the Lord of the Storytellers, The Loosener's
Brother. We call his words to make a bridge
Between the furtive questions of humans and the
Final statements of the gods.

We give you fate,
But you make your destiny

And the bull bangs his hoof
And the bull bangs his hoof
And the bull bangs his hoof

✳✳✳

The Birth of Hermes

Muse! Awakener!
Rapacious inspirer
Of a thousand good things.

We seek your fire to engorge,
Irradiate and elucidate this story
Of the gleeful son of Zeus and Maia,

Fleet of foot and swift of speech,
Stone-Cold-God of the Storytellers:
Hermes himself.

Twice great, thrice great,
A hundred times over great.

On snowy Olympus when night would fall, Zeus would slip from the vigilant gaze of Hera, his wife, and go visit his lover, the shy cave nymph Maia, Maia of the marvellous tresses. As Hera was claimed by pale-armed sleep, Zeus gleefully made his way down the mountainside to the shady part of town. No one knew, not the gods, the humans, not even the shaggy sheep on the hills, that he lingered most delightfully in the nimble arms of Maia.

(Come, come, stop tutting. Zeus' eruptive horniness is an asset to the world. It's from where all creation springs)

Maia of the cave welcomed Zeus ecstatically and inventively, and soon a spark from the mighty god's anvil leapt up and illuminated the gorgeous darkness between her hips. After nine months a child was born, a boy, tiny Hermes.

Come on sweet lips
The whole wild world
Is waiting
For your rocking and rolling

Hermes didn't waste a moment being any conventional kind of cherub. As soon as his mother rested and he had a moment to himself, he leapt up and went looking for his brother Apollo's vast herds of cattle. Being born is a hungry business. And he was desirous of the cattle. He fixed his mind on them.

At the entrance to the cave he came across a tortoise, and an idea started to glow in his mind. He picked it up and took the beast indoors. He killed it, scraped out the flesh and admired the shell. He then applied some cut reeds here, applied a cowhide and some sheep gut strings there, fixed a yoke and an arm and, of a sudden, he had invented the first lyre.

He struck it with a flat pick and the sound was good.

Amongst the idylls he immediately composed was a lively song of his own conception, intimate gossip on the love talk of Zeus and Maia, even the cauldrons and pots that belonged to the servant of Maia. It all burst forth: loudly, audaciously and un-confidentially across the valleys and dales.

But god almighty, what the kid wanted was meat. Not baby food, not a Farley's rusk, but great slabs of meat.

Meat! Meat! Meat!

His first look out at the world was promising for a thief: as he wobbled down the side of the hill he spotted the chariot and horses of Helios wearily descending under the earth for another day. Night is an ally to a light-fingered one. But even that could not distract him from getting to the shadowy mountains of Pieria where the holy cattle grazed near their stables.

The baby liberated fifty cattle from his brother's herd and drove them in a zig zaggy direction, even backwards to mix up their dusty hoof prints and evade their capture. He'd tied together some myrtle twigs and tamarisk to make some sandals. As this mad scene paraded past, his shenanigans were spotted by a man establishing his vineyard, a man by the name of Battus. Hermes spoke:

Hey old guy!

That's endless and lip-smacking wine you'll enjoy
If you didn't see me here right now
And you didn't hear me talking to you

Vat after vat after merry vat of the stuff
You'll enjoy for this confidentiality
Glug glug glug in the tangling vines

In a little while he packed the herd into a stable, and, as they chewed on sweet ginger and fresh lotus, he gathered wood to make fire. But how to make fire? The baby trimmed a laurel branch with a blade and turned it vigorously on a block of wood till it started to smoke. Then he piled up kindling and the heat and flames took hold. He didn't invent fire, but he found a way to make it.

Soon he took two cattle and slaughtered them, and had them on spits roasting. He divided them up and chose sacrificial cuts for all twelve of the gods, not for himself after all. Oh but he hungered.

He got back to the cave as dawn broke, jumped into his swaddling, sucked his thumb, burbled happily and pretended to act his age. Dark-eyed Maia was having none of it:

You are the double-sneak!

Your father wished you as a disrupter to
Both gods and humans and here you are.

I'd rather have Apollo whisk you off
Bound tight in ropes
Rather than you gadding about in the woods

Up to mischief.

Hermes broke from character and the two argued on. But down the hill aways, as time went by Apollo noticed the missing cattle and, under questioning, the man from the vineyard started to fill in the vital organs of the mystery—of a babe with a staff, zig zagging his precious cattle. Apollo soon noticed a wide-winged bird in the sky, and realised the midget thief was a child of Zeus. He was baffled and intrigued by the mess of hoof prints.

Long horn cattle
Stride backwards into a field of daffodils!
And these others: Lion or Wolf or Centaur?
What weirdness is this?

When he made his way to Maia's cave, Apollo found it replete with three hidden sanctuaries of nectar and ambrosia, chests of gold and silvery dresses, quite wonderful, with the smirking baby god all wrapped up in sweet-smelling blankets, butter wouldn't melt in such a mouth.

A battle of words pursued, with Hermes suggesting Apollo check his mental health for implying a baby less than a day old could steal his cattle—of course blowing his own cover by taking part in the debate at all. He even claimed he didn't know what a 'cow' was, being so small and all.

The greater the fabrication, the more Hermes's eyes twinkled, the more he arched his brows and let out elongated whistles at his own imaginings. He was hugely impressed by himself. No one ever accused Hermes of being a poker face. He wanted Apollo to delight along with his ebullient riffing. There was no con present. The more he swore at innocence, the more he giggled, until Apollo swept him off for a reckoning in front of their father Zeus on white-tipped Olympus.

It was a long walk to dad's house. It's always a long walk to dad's house.

Apollo working like a lawyer to trip Hermes's story up, not realising yet that Hermes's art form was to endlessly turn trips to skips. Hermes for his part gleefully smiled along at his brother's glassy eyed analysis and continued his zig zagging with wheedling anecdotes and wily rhetoric.

Apollo laid out the facts of the matter to
Zeus, the cloud compeller
In the manner of a police report,

Statistically accurate but
So dry, dry as the toast
Of a Puritan's breakfast

Dry as a scratchy cough
At the back of the scratchiest throat
Of the worst teacher of philosophy
There ever was, anywhere

But all suspected he was correct in account

Ah, but denial's not just a river in Egypt.

Like a tiny James Brown with a minute cape,
Hermes played to the gallery, played to the servants,
Played to the gods, and most of all, his father.

At his greatest denial of the theft of the cattle,
As he swore acquittal on this bully's demands,
He actually winked his eye to his father
And feebly clutched his blanket like a cherub.

Zeus delighted in his new son's storying, praised him, but sent them off to find Apollo's cattle. When Apollo attempted to bind Hermes with willow bands, he found he was unable, they simply fell away onto the ground and immediately started to sprout.

To soothe the moment, Hermes struck up the lyre, and Apollo laughed with delight, even feeling a longing in his own attentive soul for something he couldn't name. And Hermes sung too, of the gods and the muses and the troubled earth. Of the sorrow and joy of the whole messy game. And as Hermes sung, Apollo began to feel the weight and truth of the Child's vocation:

That sound was worth losing fifty cattle for.

Apollo swore affectionate protections on the baby, and that Hermes would be a guide to the gods that cannot die, and that luck would always follow him. For his part, Hermes gave Apollo the lyre, saying:

You have a gift for corralling speech elegantly
This lyre will be a clear-voiced friend

If a wise man plucks with skill
His mind will be opened to pleasure

But if struck by a brute
It will mislead and confuse him

Play with ease and delight
It dislikes being pushed around

With this, Apollo handed Hermes his shining whip and he became Keeper of Herds: looking after the concerns of the roving cattle, and that the cows would mate with the bulls and the summering meadows would be happily filled with bullocks and heifers. Before his departure, Apollo also swore an even greater oath for Hermes.

I gift you the wand
Of the three gold branches

And all the mad fortune and wealth
That comes with it

Such is your love of prophecy
I will place you in the presence

Of the Bee Maidens
Who tell the truth of things

When honey is in their mouths
And the spirit glows within them

All deeper prophecy only
Our father knows.

Hermes, son of Maia
Care for the loyal donkey

And the fiery-eyed lion
And the twist-horned cattle

Be lord of white-toothed boars
And lively flocks of sheep

And you, Hermes, you will be the
Only messenger to the Underworld

Where Hades gives the deepest gift
And takes none in return.

✳✳✳

Apollo showed his grace and care in these bindings.

And this story here, this is how Hermes walks amongst the gods, the ones who do not die, and human beings, who must.

Farewell for now King Storyteller,
Though I suspect it is you that
Has spun this tale about yourself.

Chapter Seventeen

Into the Marvellous

"Real love is one that triumphs lastingly, sometimes painfully, over the hurdles erected by time, space and the world."
Alain Badiou

And in the morning they walk to the centre of the Cista Mystica. Over the glittering scales of the serpent and the smooth roads of the bull's ivory tusks they walk. Past the maenads and the Orkney bards and the Ghanian praise singers. Past Ginsberg and Cohen, past Gawain and Rhiannon, past Tristan and Isolde, those two healed at last. There are flashes of music in the air, and bright sounds of gossip and laughter. And they come to a cave. With grapes that flush to fullness when you but gaze upon them. With wide beaked sea-ravens glorious in the sweet green pines, but an altar collapsed and no libation anywhere.

At the centre of every ritual is always a great forgetting that only you can amend. It's always been that way.

Our motley gang set to work, forging brushes from the shrubbery, gathering wild flowers and unloading the king's wine from the raft. They light incense, sweep and sing: Yiddish, Rom, Gaelic, even Chukchi songs swim up and into the ancient chamber. Father sings old Scottish hymns and no one seems to mind, least of all the gods.

Up above, Helios notices the restoration and increases his rays so they pay for their prayers with hard sweat, but down below Poseidon is touched, and cools his emerald waters for their bathing. And in the swaying fields, Demeter walks with Dionysus, and they elbow Hermes to bring music to their dedicated labours. From nowhere and everywhere, a flute is played.

As dusk comes, it seems all is set. They have made a Temenos for the Swan Lady of the Southern Quarter. The wine is poured, the altar repaired, swept and cleaned the temple. They have made a prayer of their effort, an acuity of their passion, an echolocation of their longing.

And in the hazy time, across the blue smoke, and shudderations of time she comes. Through the lays of the Troubadours she comes, from the Sonnets she comes, from the cry of Aretha Franklin she comes. From every teenager standing under every street lamp ever she comes.

Bow your head bow your head bow your head

All bury their heads in a delicious terror, an agonising ecstasy. They hide, all of them hide, the man and the girl-becoming-woman, all of them. She is too much, too great, too full.

And owl-eyed Athena comes, and blows courage into their hearts.

"Gaze up good travellers, gaze up. She who is with you always, in the very exfoliations of the world and its hurts and blisses bids you gaze up. You few, you untethered, you un-colonised, you arrivers at the Gates of Dawn.

Hear her story, and know her education. Her Temenos itself will speak the story. These libations, old stones, perfumed winds. All are in their speaking."

Suddenly the sad man, his life black sticks on the shore is afraid of this last story. Because the one he loves is suddenly screamingly, agonisingly present. The whole aggregate affair cracks and booms around him, like ice breaking mournfully out at sea. The northern gods moaning through snow, Odin screaming with his one-eyed knowledge, Orpheus risking a glance back. And the man is mad and alone. He is ruined.

There is no beeswax for his ears. And isn't that what love does? Removes all padding between you and the brute beauty of the world in all its unbearable fucking wonder?

This terrible yoga of the heart, this stretch and strain, disorder, betrayal, obsession, bliss and abandonment. This spooky laboratory of possession states, this lonely asylum of maniac feeling. And here she is, the Swan Queen behind the whole terrible ride, right in front of him.

Fuck. This is how we get made. If we survive it this is how we get made.

He remembers an old song and quietly croons the first line over and over again:

First time ever I saw your face
First time ever I saw your face
First time ever I saw your face

The story begins. Not told by the Goddess, but by the whole island—the wondrous basket itself, the Mystica. The world it writhes with holy snakes. It always did.

And the man is on the beach again, a little boy, watching the older ones risk it all for love of a girl, out to Black Rock. Oh Moon Enchanted Sea.

Alright. Holy Mother. Finish it. Take all of me. Take it fucking all.

✳✳✳

Psyche and Eros

The Track of the Moon

Inside you there are three daughters. Daughters of a King and Queen. The older two move easily into their roles—they enjoy them: the easy flirtation at parties, the diplomacy, the occasional tryst in the midnight garden, the honouring of daily tasks that delight parents and the court that circles around them.

They add a pretty note to life's music.

They are links in an ancient chain, affirming the culture. They know their story, its dance steps, its conclusion. But the youngest is something else again. Her beauty is of a different strain—it sends a shivering bell out into the world.

A track of moon on water, a vast troubling to the steady life, a wild doe with flowered hooves. Amongst the blue grey pines shepherd boys lose their minds with sheer possibility. Milk surges from dark soil when she strolls by; honey oozes in raw spurts from the bark of an alder tree.

Her name? Psyche.

We love her like the trembling foal loves sunlight, or the bliss of the ox as it lays in fresh hay. A feeling as fierce as the life-bite of the wolf cub on its mother's dark nipple. Behind her, churning through her, the yellow breast of the moon, her feet splashed silver with morning dew, glitter-hoofed from her ankle bracelets.

She wears garlands of the wild one—ivy, oak and bryony flowers, like the Bacchae that follow Dionysus. But her bones, her lashes, the mole on her cheek—all are human. She will wither, grow brittle and die, just like animals—like the great antlered herds of the forests of the far north.

Human.

But some old song is being sung through the girl, way beyond her own spell-making. In the cities, loose garlands of flowers blaze pink, yellow, red-ochre on the dust trails in front of her. People forget who they are when she's around. They gnash teeth, wind dog-rose through their curls, lay long-favoured treasures casually at her feet. Try telling *them* she's human. But at the centre of this belling storm is a grief.

As her sisters easily marry, the strength of Psyche's otherness keeps lovers from approaching her—from playful jokes at the court dance, from those hot fumbles in the summer grasses. It's more than bashfulness on the part of the men, but an iron divide. She is distanced from living. Worshipped, but distanced.

✳✳✳

Tigers of Wrath

Over time, all quarters of the earth are filled with news of her. The waves crow her form, and press their message on the rough lips of Ireland's coast, and onwards, to the deep forests of the Spear-Danes. Even sea-bandits drag moonlit verse from their jaw, to loosen up the Moorish harbours. Cattle sheltering from rain in darkling byres gossip, in their fat-tongued way, of her. The ice steppes of the Inuit forge her face in the crusted snow.

The whale-road that led Aphrodite's pilgrims to her temples of Cythera and Paphos, no longer carry the bleached sail and hopeful timber of the old devotees. These lovers of the Goddess of Love have changed allegiance. Aphrodite's temples are slurried with disinterest, they are crumbled pits, weed dens, un-roofed nests for baleful wolves. Gold long stolen, altar split, the wine brackish. Every day new seekers flood into Greece, from the Hindu Kush, Iran, the distant Orkneys, all adrift in the possibility of a moment in the presence of the young girl.

From her place of deep seeing, Aphrodite smears the ash from dead fires in abandoned temples on her face and shrieks. She, Ocean Bringer, divine energy behind Horse Dove Swan. One that has caused men to rip their hearts from their chest in the very love-havoc she invokes.

She accepts *those* offerings.

Breasts tight with desire, paps as weapons, as lusty peaks, not for the quiet suckling of a child. A ripple of curves, open-mouthed always, pearled teeth, hair a smoky nest of foam. She who demands respect from every bright corner of Olympus. From Zeus to Hera: all intone her name.

Her well-wrought crown of gold, her swan-white skin, the intricate necklace of silver that covers her throat: all are sung clear to the directions by earth's poets. Whenever a maid grows coy with deceit for love of a man, she is present—this has always been her portion from the heavens.

And this little bitch takes my place?

She calls her son, Eros, to her.

Eros—the intoxicator, dark shaker, one that brings desire to an innocent heart, horror-bringer to the ordered life, trouble-arrowed. Her son has no mind for law or tradition, scattering marriage bonds with laughter, when he loosens the black sticks from his throbbing bow. As likely to let fly at the gods as at humans, her firm-winged boy is feared. She leads him to Psyche's very door.

"I bind you with all the conditions that have led to our deadly joining as mother and son. Avenge this mucky wrongdoing. This little runt is drunk on what is mine. This is not for a human to hold, it's too much. Loosen your shaking madness— make her fall in love with a man with no social standing, no money, no house: a tramp, a wolf-person, throttled with disease, dead to honour, misery his pillow. That would be fitting."

With that, she kissed him long on the lips, with parted mouth.

When he beheld Psyche, in the moonlight of her room, for a second his finger brushed the tip of his own arrow, and he fell into love's furies for the very woman he was meant to destroy.

He could do nothing.

✳✳✳

Black Hill Wedding

None the wiser, Psyche walks the core of her life in loneliness. Hating the gifting, the mad displays on every street, the eager whoring of her subjects' dignity. She falls into a crow-slump, cannot be roused by lively wit or the court singers' lofty tune. Her brokenness radiates out into the corn, the curly ram, the long grass, the brooding storm, and all ails—the land is sick.

Her father, the king, shuffles to the temple of Apollo, leaves offerings and peers into the blue smoke hoping for instruction on the mess. On demand from Aphrodite, Apollo delivers hard news; relaying the dictate that Psyche should be taken to a lonely crag, high above the city. There, in full regalia, she would be married to a dragon lover, something scaly and deeply vile, its loyalty only to death. Though a marriage, she should wear the gear of a funeral.

An otherworldly woman was to take an otherworldly husband.

She is prepared for her funeral wedding.

The torches' flames splutter low under the moody clouds and light rain, clogged with soot no one bothers to clean. The sweet wedding tunes are not heard; the singing is of a melancholy, broken tone. The whole city is a shroud to the coming ghastly. All market square trading, all business, is cancelled. The brothels closed, the boats empty of fish. When the black trail of mourners have led Psyche to the crag, their very tears extinguish the torches.

Psyche addressed them: "Why weep now? You should have wept for me when men and women shuffled after me like a Goddess, when they laid bowls of milk at my feet, when no lover warmed my bed. When they called me the new Aphrodite, *then* you should have wept. Indeed I am clear: it is being named as Aphrodite that has caused this."

With that, the macabre troop retreat, with their greasy drum thump, and discordant whistles, to leave her to her scaly fate, her coming darkness. Alone. She stands at the very edge of the crag for many hours alive in the liminal, feet ready to plunge. In the smoky haze she thinks she can hear the blue winged approach of the One-That-Carries-Death.

She steps out.

A sweet wind fights through the bundled dark surrounding her, and lifts her on its humours. In this troubled churn, she is taken from firm ground to the impossibility of flight. The wind is sly not grand, Zephyr itself, but enough to take her down slowly from the skulled crag, down to its very base, a grassy blue bed of herbs, a-glisten still with morning dew. She moved from a night to a day.

Breathing in the scent, warmth from the world's candle, the sun gently pulls the terror free from her heart; sleep curls her shape and her eyes close.

✳ ✳ ✳

The God-House

She woke.

She found her feet led through tall trees and by a bubbling stream till she beholds a god-house, a palace so ornate it could not be crafted by human hand. Ceiling hewn in sandalwood and ivory, beasts of forest and foamy ocean prowling, silver carved and embossed on walls— walls bright-glowed with gold. The floor is nested with ruby, sapphire, diamond; the whole affair hums of divine energies. Sheep, goat and red deer skin casually lie on chairs studded with amethyst and emerald, ornately patterned with hunting scenes, and star constellations. A fire in each corner roars merrily in keen excitement.

Beauty from the whole divine world is gathered:

Fishing nets piled up in the corner, from the green teeth of Galway Bay. Antelope hide, spotted, light tan from the Sahara. The dragon-prow of a Nordic long-ship, intricate runic script carved into its coal-black majesty. Blue Jade from the Morning Star, cacao, maize, red shells rest easy on the cloak of Quetzalcoatl. As she wanders from treasure to treasure, she hears a kind of singing. Voices unseen speak comfortingly from the humming air.

"These treasures are yours. Please relax, bathe, and then let us feed you."

Hands from nowhere wash her, massage her, dress her. Afterwards, she rests, radiant on a couch shaped like a crescent moon. Any food and drink—lamb, venison, fruits from the garden, a glass of firm wine, appears even at the thought of it. Musicians beyond sight lift sound in great honeyed bundles to spray as dusted-gold into her delighted ear. When finally she retires and beds in amongst the sheets, she hears another voice. Male.

A playful growl, a forested murmur, an echo of a world beyond even this. And hands come, hands that coax curly delight from her writhing body.

For the first time, she takes a lover.

She slept as never before. Towards dawn, the dark one slips from the chamber, never revealing more than voice, scent and touch, his appearance a mystery. And so it goes. During the day this life of choired voices, dappled light in the god-house, a lifted spirit. And at night the joyous churn of the sheets.

Something slumbers in the breathing beside her.

This lover? Eros. Who has loved her since his first glimpse. Who could not obey his mother's demand. Eros, whose ear, many months into their time together, catches on the wind the worry of Psyche's parents, gut-sore at the black wedding, and the swift arrival of her two older sisters now married—back home to offer comfort to the frail pair who are awash with sticky guilt at the selling of their girl to fate's wrathful dictates.

Eros whispered to his lover, "The Fates are singing cruelly and thrashing the bull-skin drum, aiming a distinguished malice in your direction. Pot stirrers.

Your sisters will gather at the ledge from which the wind picked you. They will search hard for you. But know this: any contact will flail joy from your body, will render me wracked and broken, set a-flame our settled nest."

But the thoughts of that human contact, those old sibling ties, made her weep for the simple things that could not be met in the god-house.

She pushed hard, made an art of her grief until Eros relented, and agreed that the sisters' concern must be met, that they would be brought to the palace, laden with gifts, but that Psyche must not speak of their relationship as the sisters' council would be a dark seed, a rotting egg, a festered gifting of their own ambitions.

✳✳✳

Up in the crag-world, the sisters thrashed their chests and sent out a baleful wail that echoed from the eagle-high rocks. The grief-sound caught Psyche's ear and she called on that sly wind to lift them down from the death-space to trees and fruit, and silvered lakes, to the god-house.

The more beauty they ate, the hungrier they became. Inside this shimmer-castle they grew squat with malice, hollowed green with envy to have this abundance for themselves. As enquiry on Psyche's lover rained down, she claimed him a youth, a wealthy hunter, who spent much time in the forested comb of the nearby hills, a lover of the bone-white moon, a man that sings animals to his very breast.

Then she clammed up.

She ladled them with rings, heavy brooches, necklaces, and called the wind to lift their sweating feet back to their gossipy lives. Off, off, off you go.

✳✳✳

Once settled on the high stone, the sisters hurled black judgment on Psyche. "Pompous ass! Lording it over us—her *older* sisters. Wasn't it always this way?"

The eldest: "My man is older than our father, crow-bald, so diminished in grandeur, so cock-less he keeps our jewels under heavy lock. Gutless. No panache."

The next: "And mine—stiff in bone, and bent in back he is, like a freak of the travelling people. It has been many years since I felt his charms in the dark. All youth is long drained from me, as I massage dung-smelling medicines into his yellowed husk. He has robbed me of myself."

The two resolved to keep Psyche's glories from their parents, and in fact to bring sweet ruin to their little sister's life.

✳✳✳

Eros's prophetic ear gathered this messaging, knew their sows-nest was dunged with schemes and relayed their baying plans to Psyche. "Beloved. They send a fist of trouble to unseat us. You must know that our loving has caused a spark of light to leap in the den of your womb, a child is growing there. If you keep quiet on the intricacies of our love it will be divine, if you blurt all to the four directions it will be mortal—and, in time, wither and die."

A deep glow came to Psyche's being at the news of the babe. Stars aligned, foamy shores spun turquoise waves.

✳✳✳

Again the sisters visited. Again, through old, familiar threads, they convinced Psyche they meant no harm—none at all. In fact, witnessing her changing shape, they grew pretend-joyful and claimed this would be wonderful news for their parents, surely the child would be like some kind of god! As great as Eros!

They don't know what they are saying.

They lounge about, munching grapes, scrubbed clean by the unseen hands, pink and pearly, but always closing in on their perennial question: "Who is the lover?" Psyche forgets her first fabrication, and now spins a few lines about him being a man in middle-years, who trades in far off countries.

Indeed, indeed.

As the sisters are again deposited on the coal-black crag, they gossip on her lies.

"She doesn't know what he looks like! He must be a god or fairy-souled. We must bend our heads together, sister, grow our craft to a new height, to scupper this little witch. Tomorrow we shall return to her side."

On the third visit they convinced her that her night-man was a dragon-lover, an enchanter, and has been seen at dusk by shepherds approaching the house. A foul thing, deadly. They say that when Psyche is approaching full term this beast will consume both her and the baby. Gobbled, even the bones. They left her with a lantern, and strong persuasion to light it on the slumbering beast, and in that dull light to sever his head from his shoulders. With a sword then produced, they webbed gossip and fear as a necklace around ivory-faced Psyche.

Content that she was both petrified and intending to act on their advice they scuttled that tireless wind back to the comfort of their own dwellings.

Heartsick but clear, she hid the devices in the few shadows the house had.

That night, after love, he drifted into the long breath of sleep. She lit the lantern and committed to gazing. She beheld his curls, lips, even his swan-white wings reaching from his shoulders. Her man was a God of Love.

The God of Love.

Curiously handling an arrow from his quiver, she pressed on the very tip, immediately breaking skin. Love's ecstasies saddled her hips and heart, delirium beat its high note as she deepened again into amor. As she whimpered her desires into his ear, as she clamped down onto his brightness she started the lamp swinging so as to catch his face in the light.

One bolt of hot oil
flew onto his right shoulder.

A blurring of feathers and shout, the god awoke. Exposed, betrayed, lucid in his rage, already flapping for the window. Psyche gripped his muscled thigh as he hurled himself into the black night. As all lovers do, she fell. Onto warm soil, but she fell. For a moment Eros hovered in the high branches of a cypress tree, damaged.

"I blame myself.
I who fell for the very woman
my mother told me to curse.

I, desire's hunter—the archer, the high man—caught in my own net of longing. To be with a woman who mistakes me for a beast, whose false sisters equip her with lantern and blade, disaster's pilgrims. Well, they have succeeded. Find out what it is to live without love."

He lifted, crashing through the emerald bough
and was gone.

✻✻✻

Oblivion messaged in her ear, to end the tearing heart adrift in her chest. She ran to a stream and threw herself in, but the very denizens of the swirling grey waters lifted her out, and lay her on its banks, safe amongst wildflowers in full bloom.

Looking on were Pan and Echo. He, the hoofed-god of the shepherds, the belly-haired, Arcadian lover of the sun-warm copse—she, the nymph of mountain, free wanderer of meadow and trail, always bidden to reply when another cries.

He speaks: his fluty croak rich with the gurgle of the waters and a hundred secret things.

"With my divining powers,
my steely gaze, my furry knowledge,
I see you are in wild distress.
Your stumbles, your wax-cheek,
your bloodshot eyes, tell me you are stricken
in the net of love in excess.

You are mad, out of balance. I know something about this.

Cease this flirtation with death. Take yourself to Eros the god—his arm is muscled but his heart soft. Give him good prayer, right from the belly, be clear with your longings and he will forgive."

She takes the words like food and staggers off. Her thoughts turn to those very sisters that caused this state. Revenge. One by one, she journeys to their kingdoms and tells them that her lover was indeed a god, in fact Eros himself.

That he was so furious with her lantern and blade, he has abandoned her, and commanded the wind to drop her here at the sister's door. That he has chosen that sister to be his bride—one he could trust. Each one, aflame to lay a god, to be raised in rank, to gloat in the stink of riches, tells her husband her parents have died, and takes herself off to the black crag. Trusting the winds, on different days they step out.

Ah, but it is a sly wind. Two times, the fall.

Bodies crumpled, mashed, gut splattered over the sizzling rocks, a goodly feast for the lion and the eagle.

✳✳✳

Aphrodite

Aphrodite is bathing in the creamy foam of the sea, laughing as the current drags her under, then over, the bruise-coloured waves, to the numbing ink depths and then up to the shore-breakers glistening with the sun's generosity. A bird comes with news. That Eros, her son, is resting, sick at her home.

That he has taken a lover, the very one she ordered him to destroy. "That whore of the street is my son's lover?" The bird confirms this. And adds that whilst her son is sick with the oil's wound, and she bathes oblivious, all the world's lovers are disconnected and squabbling— they can find no sharing ground, but make chaos and enjoy not a moment of harmony; disrepair is amok.

Without these two constants of love, it is all mud, smoke and darkness. She hurries to his chamber and sets about him with a furied tongue:

"Forever you have flung your arrows, making us all into love dogs, sniffing the chests of illicit booty, wandering lusty orchards as dawn breaks, howling as the light comes, pissing on the good bonds of steady marriage, even the elders will walk a hundred miles for a fumble with some new sweetheart.

It's embarrassing—this power of yours. And you have enjoyed the reckless flailing of your arrow-bounty, admit it. But now you are struck by your own malaise, and will enter a covenant of suffering, a settling of loneliness that will mark hard your handsomeness.

I will put you in the tutelage of ancient Sobriety—little enough you have cared for her company these many years. She will temper your quick hand, clip that flowing hair, bind those wings so keen to ascend. Feed you grit and harsh instruction, show you stewardship, un-do this queasy grandeur."

And so it was, that sick Eros entered the instruction of old Sobriety.

✳✳✳

Psyche

On her path, Psyche left good gifts and time and energy at the temples of Demeter and Hera—Queens of earth and heaven. At Demeter's she gathered scattered offerings and gave them shape, ritual form—the ears of barley, piled wheat, sickles, dumped by locals as careless offerings. At Hera's, the grandness of the offerings and holy feeling to the place made her bend her head and call prayer.

But neither deity would help—they were tender, and sent kind words but would not cross the will of Aphrodite. She was on her own.

Finally she arrived at the very door of Aphrodite. Met by Old Habit, a servant, she was dragged by the hair, spat on, beaten and degraded, towards the Goddess of Love.

The Great One shrieked a rook-laugh when she beheld the raggle-taggle girl before her.

"A little late, don't you think? To send respects to your mother-in-law? No matter. I will bring you into the tutelage of Anxiety and Grief, as a sign of my good will. A wedding gift as it were. They have great fistfuls of instruction for one such as you."

With little regard for her growing grand-child in Psyche's belly, Aphrodite was given to ripping Psyche's clothes, clawing great handfuls of hair from her batter-sore skull, shaking her very being.

All the while many dark torments rained down from her diligent tutors—Anxiety and Grief. The schooling is thorough. In some dark corner of the same house, Eros struggles under the weight of Sobriety, but they do not meet.

✳✳✳

The Four Tasks

Aphrodite leads Psyche to a vast heap of barley, wheat, poppy seed, millet.

"Little one. You look so thrashed, so gaunt, so death-touched, I suspect my son would not come within a mile of you now. No matter. Well, if your looks are gone, let's see you find your worth in a different expression. Prove yourself. Separate every grain, every lonesome seed, in this mountain. Stack them into new, gleaming towers—and by nightfall. I have a wedding to attend and will return later."

And with that, Our Lady of Milky Sea and Lake departs. The very task froze Psyche. Hopeless.

But as she sat in the grey light, from some corner of the palace, a tiny ant appeared and in its diligent way, started to separate out the grains. No drama, no great display, just focused work. Soon many thousands of ants come, a black line of energy across the golden floor, making good, line by line, the chaos.

Only when every single grain was resplendent in golden and brown heaps did the helpers retreat back into the shadows of the room. Aphrodite returned later, woozy with booze, flower arrayed, the love-stink of exotic perfume loosened from the pores of her skin. Seeing the piles in dusky light, she spoke:

"Your hand did not weave this. Some animal power, some occult chant enlisted this accomplishment. So be it. We shall still see what you can do." She chucked a loaf of old, black bread at the girl, and sauntered to bed. At dawn the next day, Psyche is summoned, and Aphrodite points with a languid hand: "There is a grove in this direction. A grove that touches the edge of silvery water—it is a stream that comes down from the mountain, with fat berry bushes hanging over its bank.

In that place are lively sheep. Sheep that carry fleeces of gold. I am desirous of that gold. Bring me a wisp or two of that glowing wool. Get on with it."

Psyche knows all about those lively sheep. Lively sheep? They are razor-toothed rams, furious in the Mediterranean heat, hellish-jaws ready to clamp and rupture, stone-skulled, poised to butt and maim, charged-hooves, bone-breakers, mercy-deniers. Archaic guardians of their glittered coat. They will not go easy.

As thoughts of oblivion reared again, as she contemplated the violence of suicide standing on a crag edge overlooking the waters, she heard music.

A weird, fluty sound—like the pipes of that old shepherd god, Pan. It was a river reed, singing advice:

"Step back from this dying. Take courage. This is all about the business of patience. The terrifying heat of the sun sends the rams blood-crazy. To approach them now would speed you to the Underworld. This is not what you want or need. Later, in the afternoon, a breeze comes, and the streams sing the steam off their mighty backs, weaving some tenderness into the red coals of their hearts.

They will fall into a slumber, delighted by the cool. Then, and only then, is the moment to come quietly from the tree line and gather the golden wisps that have scattered the nearby briars and bushes." She followed the reed's wisdom, and in the cooling of the day glided by the slumbered rams and gathered enough wool to fill her arms from elbow to elbow.

Aphrodite accepted the gift, "I know this comes from collaboration. Some unseen force has reached out to you. But what of your courage? Your prudence? I have another task.

Follow my pointing finger—there in the distance is a high mountain—not just any mountain.

At its great peak is an opening to the Underworld. From there a stream of utter darkness rushes with its horrors, down the slope to flood the Stygian marshes, and spreads out into the grief streams of Cocytus. I am giving you a small urn, that I wish you to take to the river's very mouth, up on the peak, where you will gather up some of its water for my pleasure.

Simple, really."

The mountain was not easy for the climbing. It held its upward navigation close to its chest. The rocks were scalding to the touch, dragons swooshed here and there. Paths crumbled under foot and sent pebbles and bramble to the dark spread of water below.

Some instinct told her one splash of the water would end her. So how to fill the urn? Again she was frozen by the enormity of the task. But Zeus's great bird, the eagle, flew by:

"You are *green*, woman: naive. To think that any human could get near that current. Even Zeus blanches at the mention of the Styx River. Give me the urn."

She reached up in the air, and the vast bird picked up the small pot with its immense talons. The dragon defied his demise with deadly, unblinking eyes; the river spat warning in gurgled speech, that one fleck of moisture on feather would be enough.

But he voiced the strangeness of his task, of Aphrodite's place in it—a divine errand, and he bent back the bars of the death river's ambitions, made sweet the impossible, and filled the urn. Sometime later, wild-eyed but joyful, Psyche handed over the jar to the Ocean Bringer herself.

✳✳✳

Underworld

Aphrodite looks hard at the woman in front of her. Takes her in, top to toe.

"Are you a hedge-witch? A sorceress?

Impressive, certainly.

Well, woman. I have one last task for you. Judging by how you glided through the others, this should be of little consequence to such a conjurer, a power-eater, as yourself. Your path is downwards now. Underworld. Past tree roots and minerals, past dripping caves and mouldy bones, past hope, down to the dwelling of Hades. Find Persephone. Send her my greetings, and ask for a small portion—just a day's worth—of her beauty potion. Having spent so much time attending to my sickly son, I am depleted, and need restoration from a deep place. In this task you must be swift, as I need the portion before I attend the great theatre at Olympus."

Psyche felt the sentence land as heavy iron. So laced with horror, this trip to hell— she could never achieve this final requirement.

Climbing a high tower, she again prepared to end her life. The tower itself spoke:

"Why end when you are so near completion? Much is hidden from you, but your hard miles churn good grapes under your feet. Wine of strong flavour is your legacy. I have instruction:

At the dark edge of the city of Lacedaemon is Taenarus, a hidden place.

Go there. You will find a cave—summon your courage and enter it. Men will try and stop you. They will tell you nameless creatures linger in its depths, that these lanterned men are the last gate. That no word is ever returned of those who go further. Ever. You will go in. In that hazy place you will move between worlds. Follow the path, it will lead you directly to Hades.

It is vital that you bring two barley cakes, and that you carry two gold coins tight between your teeth.

On this Underworld path you will meet an old man, lame, loading a limping donkey with wood. He will ask you to help him with just a few branches that have fallen to the ground. Do not. Eventually you will reach the death-river, Styx. The ferryman, Chiron, will demand payment. He must take the coin directly from your mouth, not your hand.

Whilst crossing the black sludge, a dead man will emerge from the terror-waters, begging you to pull him aboard. Do not. That would violate the Underworld's laws.

At the far shore you will encounter three women, busy weaving the web of fate. They will encourage you as a sister to join them, to take up their work with the cloth.

Do not.

To touch that cloth is forbidden.

All these lures are about getting you to drop those barley cakes—those cakes you need to feed to terrible Cerebus, the three-headed hound that keeps immortal watch on Persephone's palace. So give him the food. Get yourself past as the three heads squabble for crumbs, and into the presence of Persephone.

She will offer you a chair and food—a dazzling feast—but accept neither; sit low on the dirt floor and ask for a piece of bread. Deliver the message and she'll give you what you ask for. When returning, throw another cake to the dog, let Chiron pull gold from between your teeth, and get back up that path to this world as fast as you possibly can.

Do not pause, do not look left or right, and, of course, under no circumstances look in that box."

Loaded with advice, a structure appearing in what had been overwhelming chaos, she gathered the cakes and coins and set out.

She found the cave, took the path, ignored the lame man and his request, paid Chiron by the coin between her teeth, looked away from the pleadings of the river corpse, rejected the entreaties of Fate's weavers, threw vittles to the three-headed slobbering hound, found herself at the feet of the Underworld Goddess.

She rejected the handsome seat, the candled-feast, scented and herbed, the ruby goblet, the great puddings, and, squatting on bony dirt, asked for one piece of bread. She sent Aphrodite's request and handed over a small casket that was filled by Persephone, in some far-off place.

With grateful thanks she took the box and departed the shuddering gloom of The-World-Underneath, and headed out, fast. She fed the hound with the last cake, teeth-snapping horror that it is, had the coin mouthed for the ferryman, and felt joy lift her feet as she headed for the surface.

When she broke ground, as sun hooked its charms over her breast and face, she wept and gave thanks.

As she walked, and as she began to loosen just a little of the horrors of this blackened-trip, she felt a seed of curiosity flower in her heart. What was in the box?

She had been through so much herself, surely a little of that hard-won beauty could be hers, just a touch.

For several miles she walked with this back and forth raging its speech in her tired head. She stopped. Almost at the end of her journey, just miles from the home of Aphrodite, she opened the casket.

Nothing. Empty.

She pressed her face into its absence, scouring every inch. Nothing for the eye to see. But there was something, something not for the eye. The sleep of the Underworld curled around her head, and drew her down. There, on the dusty path, she slept, into oblivion.

✳✳✳

Eros

And what of Eros?

After his heart-sick return to his mother, he had been stretched on the rack of Sobriety's instruction, had his wingtips sooted with the ash of grief, slowed his aerial pace so he knew what it was like to walk on the sad old ground of earth. Sobriety had forced his mind in one direction. When the lure of distraction had overwhelmed, when he reached for his flighty arrows, his ancient teacher gathered him, reminded him of the teary-hooves of the horse he rode. Reminded him of Psyche.

His previous feasting had been replaced by a broth, lacking glamour, but rich in goodness for both soul and body. It was this focused tutelage that had kept him apart from Psyche even when his beloved was under the same roof, undergoing her tasks.

His gold was no longer light, but polished, deeper, tempered. When he gazed out, still bent with longing from his bedroom window on the path leading to his mother's home, he took in the sight of Psyche asleep. In a fraction of a second his vast wings had thrust the very air apart in his desire to get to her side. His hand gathered, swept up the sleep-murk, like dark bees around her head, and placed it back in the box.

He then gently pricked her finger with his arrow.

"Beloved. Once you awakened me, now I awaken you. You have almost completed the task—get the box to my mother, and I will address Zeus himself to make clear our love."

On Eros's arrival at Olympus, Zeus was enthused at the clear growing of this boy, this one who had caused such havoc even to him and his canopy of lovers, had sprinkled mayhem into the gravitas of Olympus. He praised the union, and also Aphrodite for the difficult lessons taught before such a wedding can take place. She, Ocean Maker, had hurled grit and testing on these two, and with her cast of goodly instructors, forged a deepening bond.

(Scar tissue, some would say.)

Psyche was brought forward and offered nectar—a drink that when drunk made her divine—equal in every way to her husband.

The great wedding took place.

Aphrodite danced, Dionysus poured wine, Pan played his wild pipes.

All of this is going inside us, all the time.

On the mountain peaks of high Greece,
they are still cleaning up from that wedding.

✳✳✳

And for a long time the travellers sleep, with only the Piper at the Gates of Dawn to accompany them.

Coda

And the man of the Underneath wakes. His daughter wakes.

In Devon, in the cottage by the river and the forest.

A dream? A whimsy?

The dripping timbers of the raft in a very startled English garden put pay to that fantasy. Dad and kid drag the beams to the side of the lawn, breathing deeply the tang of brine.

He asks his girl to put her hand in her pocket. She pulls out a grey-green stone. Ah. Not quite yet then.

But what happened after the story? What happened? After entering the Cista Mystica?

Well, life went on, didn't it? Not the same, never the same, but it continued.

Most of the travellers went on their way, emboldened, challenged and usefully haunted.

Some walked into the hearts of children, and ruddy-cheeked bakers, and professors and mid-wives, taxi drivers and lovers and grievers. Some took their little boat and found a West Country cove to land in, others drifted back to find old, lost loves in Lithuania and the Carpathian mountains. Aphrodite has that effect. Some took the stories into prisons, and round fires with rowdy kids, some crafted them into dissertations and learnt new languages, picked up an instrument, took to the streets, found a thousand ways to joyfully participate in the sorrows of the world.

Yevgeny and Rosa fell in love, of course.

So, dear reader, what did we learn? You and I? After all that heat, and grief and bluster.

To carry gold between our teeth. To be schooled by sobriety and grief. To let ashes touch our wingtips. To go to the Underworld when we must, to party like its Olympus when we must. To not mistake a human for a goddess—or not entirely—or hide too much of ourselves in shadow. To deepen.

And the man with his funny old care, his mysterious love, the one he can't quite shrug, found his story—the whole thing—in a cave that is everywhere and nowhere, in the presence of a living goddess.

And for a little while, in his way, he knew peace.

Even as snow falls
you are lovely to me
like the
dark tents of Kedar
a sachet of myrrh
a cluster of henna blossoms
a vineyard in bloom

A hundred nights
I have visited your croft
and watched you sleeping,
chopped wood
and told you stories

My babushka.

P.S.

Dad and kid have something to report. That not quite all the travellers left the raft. Some have repaired it, and set off on other adventures. Occasionally we get a postcard.

That Blodeuedd, the Owl of Flowers, has settled quite comfortably in the forest by the cottage.

And for all you vagabondias on the caravanserai of amor (and we can see you here, filling up the cottage with your rucksacks and French wine and Rilke sonnets) keen on this sort of thing, you should know she has become quite the storyteller herself. She flies over Albion and collects things we really need to know about, weaving in and out of the dusty centuries.

Never give up on love.

The Team (without whom...)

Sedna's Comb (Inuit)
The Huntress (Inuit)
The Woman Who Became a Fox (Aleutian)
Tatterhood (Eastern European)
The Holy Couple (Jewish)
Vasya Whitefeet (Romany)
Pwyll and Rhiannon (Welsh)
Blodeuedd of the Flowers (Welsh)
Clorinda, Queen of the Shepherds (English)
Wudu-Wasa (English)
Bleak Shore (Shetlands)
The Seal-Woman (Orkney)
Cinderbiter (Scotland)
Taligvak (Inuit)
A Drum Used for Magic (Chukchi)
What Mayaki Heard at the Smokehole (Chukchi)
The Birth of Hermes (Greek)
Psyche and Eros (Greek)

*The battle of words between Hawk and Cormorant was directly inspired by a piece of bardic verse entitled, "The Dialogue of the Two Sages."

Reference List of Quotes

Badiou, A. 2009. *In Praise of Love.* Profile Books.

Gilbert, J. 2005. *Refusing Heaven.* Alfred A. Knopf.

Hillman, J. 2010. *The Red Book: Jung and the Profoundly Personal.* Symposium, The Library of Congress.

Lewis, C.S. 1961. *A Grief Observed.* Faber and Faber.

Lorca. 2019. *Courting the Dawn:Poems of Lorca,* Shaw and Harding. White Cloud Press.

Milosz, C. 2006. *New and Collected Poems 1931-2001.* Penguin.

Shakespeare. 1986. *The Sonnets and a Lover's Complaint.* Penguin.

About the Author

Dr Martin Shaw is an acclaimed teacher of myth. Author of the award-winning Mythteller trilogy (*A Branch From The Lightning Tree, Snowy Tower, Scatterlings*), he founded the Oral Tradition and Mythic Life courses at Stanford University, whilst being director of the Westcountry School of Myth in the UK. He has introduced thousands of people to mythology and how it penetrates modern life. For twenty years Shaw has been a wilderness rites of passage guide, working with at-risk youth, the sick, returning veterans and many women and men seeking a deeper life.

His translations of Gaelic poetry and folklore (with Tony Hoagland) have been published in *Orion Magazine, Poetry International, Kenyon Review, Poetry Magazine* and the *Mississippi Review*. His most recents books are *The Night Wages*, and his Lorca translations, *Courting the Dawn* (with Stephan Harding). His essay and conversation with Ai Weiwei on myth and migration was published by the Marciano Arts foundation in early 2019.